AN INTRODUCTION TO THERMONUCLEAR RE-SEARCH deals with the basic problems of controlled fusion research, and is written for the technical reader who does not, however, have a background of plasma physics. The book gives the conditions for successful controlled thermonuclear research, followed by specific reference to leading approaches to the fusion problem. Emphasis is placed on simplified derivation and qualitative understanding rather than rigor, leading to a better appreciation of the physical equations essential to fusion research.

This monograph will be particularly useful as an introduction to the fusion field and to the relevant U.S. project literature, whilst it also details the key items in the mass of recently declassified reports and documents.

INTERNATIONAL SERIES OF MONOGRAPHS ON

NUCLEAR ENERGY

GENERAL EDITORS: R. A. CHARPIE AND J. V. DUNWORTH

Division XIV   Plasma Physics and
Thermonuclear Research

VOLUME 1

AN INTRODUCTION TO THERMONUCLEAR RESEARCH

AN INTRODUCTION TO
THERMONUCLEAR RESEARCH

A series of lectures given in 1955

by

ALBERT SIMON
Oak Ridge National Laboratory

PERGAMON PRESS
LONDON · NEW YORK · PARIS · LOS ANGELES
1959

PERGAMON PRESS LTD.
4 & 5 Fitzroy Square, London, W.1.

PERGAMON PRESS, INC.
122 East 55th Street, New York 22, N.Y.
P.O. Box 47715, Los Angeles, California

PERGAMON PRESS, S.A.R.L.
24 Rue des Écoles, Paris Vᵉ

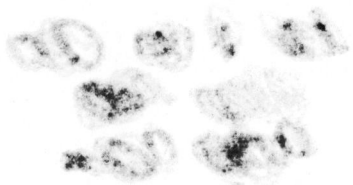

Library of Congress Card No. 59–10528

Set by Santype Ltd., Salisbury
Printed in Great Britain by Wyman and Sons Ltd.,
London, Reading and Fakenham

CONTENTS

v

PREFACE

THE material in this monograph is based in part on a series of lectures given by the author at the Oak Ridge National Laboratory in the Fall of 1955. At that time the Oak Ridge project was still quite small and limited to work on ion sources, diffusion across magnetic fields and theoretical studies. These lectures were intended for a wider audience at the laboratory; the object being the introduction of a large group to the problems basic to controlled fusion research with the hope of obtaining useful ideas and scientific assistance. The typical audience was entirely a technical one (mainly physicists with some chemists, mathematicians and engineers; all at the B.S. level or higher) and the lectures were pitched at that level.

Following the close of the lecture series there were many suggestions that it would be useful to have a writeup of the material available, and this task was begun in the Summer of 1956. The material contained in this report was expanded considerably over that given in the lectures and included some information which had become available at the Gatlinburg meeting (June, 1956) and even some items which were reported in the Fall of 1956 (Los Alamos meeting). The completed report, ORNL 2285, entitled "Nine Lectures on Project Sherwood", was finally issued late in 1956.

At the time of the second Geneva Conference, Pergamon Press suggested to the author that it would be useful to publish these lectures in substantially their original form, and this was agreed to. The material in this monograph has been changed considerably from that of ORNL 2285. Some errors have been weeded out and the presentation in the earlier chapters considerably altered for purposes of clarification and pedagogy. However, no attempt has been made to bring the material up to date. Such a task would be quite lengthy, delaying the publication of this work by many months, and would probably be partially futile since the course of research in controlled fusion seems to be a rapidly-oscillating function of time. Periods of mounting optimism are followed by periods of partial gloom. At the moment, the Pinch approach seems in dire straights due to uncontrolled instabilities, the Stellarator has unexplained losses of plasma and the most promising high-energy injection devices (DCX and OGRA) have not yet reached the critical stage of burnout which will test their futures.

It would seem that this oscillating function of time is not a random one, however, since the research programs of the U.S.A. and the U.S.S.R., revealed for the first time at Geneva, have shown a startlingly similar development in time.

Nevertheless, the basic requirements which a successful plasma must meet, have remained unchanged. So have the basic ideas underlying the Pinch, Stellarator and Mirror devices. Hence it is hoped that these lectures may yet serve a useful purpose.

Perhaps the most important items omitted as a result of the time cutoff on these lectures are the material on the molecular ion injection devices (the Oak Ridge DCX and the U.S.S.R.'s OGRA) as well as the ZETA device at Harwell and the planned substitution of helical fields for the equivalent figure-eight geometries at Princeton. Publications covering these items may be found in the reports of the Geneva Conference.

No attempt has been made to cover all the activities in the U.S. Sherwood project through 1955. Some programs have been almost entirely omitted. The relative weightings are influenced by the personal interests of the author and in no way are intended to imply a judgement as to the importance of any activity to the success of Project Sherwood.

Many thanks are due to Dr. Lyman Spitzer, Jr., for his valuable comments regarding parts of the original manuscript of ORNL 2285. Some sections of this monograph are based on material available in two reports, "Orientation Lectures", NYO 6049, by Dr. Lyman Spitzer, Jr., and "16 Lectures on Controlled Thermonuclear Reactions", UCRL 4231, by Dr. Richard F. Post. The influence of these excellent reports will be obvious throughout. In addition, the chapter on stability is based in part on a guest lecture on that subject at Oak Ridge presented by Dr. Russell Kulsrud of Project Matterhorn. Finally, I am greatly indebted to Dr. Robert J. Mackin, Jr., for his careful reading of the final manuscript and for several valuable comments.

CHAPTER I
THE POTENTIALITIES OF A FUSION REACTOR

It is certainly a natural thing, now that one has reactors operating by the fission of uranium and plutonium, to consider the possibility of obtaining energy for power plants from the exothermic reactions of the lightest elements. What is odd about this, is that this effort should have come later in time than the development of fission power. Historically, the existence of this possible source of power was known many years before fission was discovered. It was known that fusion reactions were the basic energy source of the stars.

Nonetheless, no serious attempt to explore the problems involved in tapping this energy source was made before the war. Perhaps this was partially due to psychological reasons. It must have seemed quite fantastic to consider the possibility of the release of nuclear energy on a laboratory scale rather than on an astronomical scale.

The advent of the fission process, with its convenient neutrons, changed all this. Nuclear energy was released on earth. The final step was the release of fusion energy itself, although in uncontrolled form, as the hydrogen bomb. Beginning in the early 1950s, a series of proposals for schemes to create a controlled thermonuclear reactor (CTR) have resulted in the creation of an AEC project with the overall name of Project Sherwood. Major research efforts in this field are being carried out at Princeton, Los Alamos, Livermore and Oak Ridge. Smaller scale projects exist at the Naval Research Laboratory and New York University.

The essential features of the general problems involved and some details of the individual projects will be described in the lectures to follow. The basic problem, in its utmost simplicity,

1

may be described as that of creating and containing a gas at temperatures greater than that of the sun's interior for a time long enough to achieve sizeable nuclear reactions. The first three major research centers are now working on specific schemes for a CTR. Oak Ridge has been concerned mainly with supporting research and development but is now studying the design of a possible device.

Energy resources of the Earth

It is certainly a valid first question to ask what role fusion power would play in the energy resources of this earth. This question is most easily answered by listing some data from a book by Palmer Putnam[1].

Putnam defines a convenient energy unit called the Q which has a value equal to 10^{18} BTU. In Table 1.1 we summarize some

TABLE 1.1. ENERGY USAGE

ESTIMATED CONSUMPTION

Burnup to 1850	6–9 Q
1850–1950	4
Total to 2000	25
Total to 2050	100
Present rate is 10 Q per century	

PRESENT RESOURCES

Available Coal	32
Oil	6
	38 Q
Nuclear	575

of Putnam's estimates concerning the consumption of energy on the earth, both past and future, as well as his estimates of the remaining reserves.

---

[1] P. PUTNAM, *Energy in the Future*, Van Nostrand, Princeton, N.J. (1953).

Note that the estimated consumption of fuel to the years 2000 and 2050 are based on an extrapolation of both the population growth of the planet and of the rise in energy requirements per capita.

The second part of the table summarizes the major energy resources remaining on this planet. These estimates consider only those available reserves of coal and oil which can be economically marketed—that is to say, marketed at a basic price that is not over twice the present average cost. The total reserve in nuclear fuel includes uranium and thorium and assumes complete breeding. This last number is perhaps the most uncertain of Putnam's estimates and, in fact, there is a great deal of evidence that it is an appreciable underestimate. Thus it is clear that there is no immediate and pressing urgency for the development of a fusion reactor, while there *is* good reason for a large-scale effort in the fission field. It is also clear, however, that there is certainly something less than an unlimited supply of energy in uranium and thorium, even assuming complete breeding. If the power requirements of the earth should rise appreciably above their present levels, it is conceivable that all other energy sources— that is other than fusion and solar energy—will be exhausted in a few hundred years.

What is the energy reserve which is available in light element fusion processes? To evaluate this, consider the reactions listed in Table 1.2, which, as will be seen later, comprise the most

TABLE 1.2. FUSION REACTIONS

$$D + D \longrightarrow \begin{cases} \rightarrow He^3(0.8 \text{ MeV}) + n(2.5) \\ \rightarrow T(1.0) + p(3.0) \end{cases}$$

$$D + T \longrightarrow He^4(3.5) + n(14.1)$$

$$D + He^3 \longrightarrow He^4(3.6) + p(14.7)$$

$$T + T \longrightarrow He^4(3.8) + 2n(7.6)$$

$$He^3 + He^3 \longrightarrow He^4(4.3) + 2p(8.5)$$

feasible reactions for a fusion reactor. The D–D reaction produces either a neutron or proton, each with about 50% probability. The energies of the reaction products are listed in parentheses in the table.

The energy release in the burning of deuterium may be estimated by following a deuterium atom through *all* the burnings which will occur, even in a reactor which is initially of pure deuterium. One of the reaction by-products, tritium, will be consumed in a D-T reaction. The remaining by-product, He^3, has a low cross section for reaction with a deuteron and may or may not burn before escaping from the system. This will depend on the details of the reactor. Assuming that it is consumed the energy balance is as shown in Table 1.3.

TABLE 1.3. ENERGY BALANCE

$D + D \longrightarrow T(1.0) + p(3.0)$	
$D + D \longrightarrow He^3(0.8) + n(2.45)$	
$D + T \longrightarrow He^4(3.5) + n(14.1)$	
$D + He^3 \longrightarrow He^4(3.6) + p(14.7)$	

$$6D \longrightarrow 2He(7.1) + 2p(17.7) + 2n(16.55) + (1.8)$$

The over-all effect is the burning of six deuterons. The products are two protons, two neutrons, and two alpha particles. The neutrons will carry their energy out of the gas. The energy given to the charged particles is put back into the gas since charged particles will not be expected to escape. Adding up the energy in charged particles and dividing by six shows that the energy deposited in the gas per deuteron is 4.4 MeV. Similarly, dividing the energy which escapes in the form of neutrons by six yields an additional energy contribution per deuteron of 2.76 MeV. The total energy output per deuteron burned is approximately 7.2 MeV. If the D–He^3 reaction does not occur, the yield per deuteron is only 4.7 MeV.

It is instructive to use these figures to calculate the available energy on the surface of the earth in the form of sea water. Deuterium occurs in sea water in a ratio of about 1 part in 5000. The corresponding energy in a gallon of sea water is then easily found to be of the order of magnitude of 10^4 kWh. Speaking very roughly, 1 gal of water has the energy equivalent of 300 gal of gasoline. Since an estimate for the amount of surface water on the earth is about 10^{21} gal, the total energy available from sea water is readily calculated to be about 5×10^{10} Q. Hence, if one could burn deuterium in a controlled thermonuclear reactor, the energy problems of the earth would be solved for an essentially infinite time. Incidentally, the cost of separating the amount of deuterium found in a gallon of water from sea water is approximately 10 cents, which is completely negligible.

Over and above the energy resource argument for Sherwood, there exist at least three other reasons for working on this project. The first is the possibility that a Sherwood device may supply electric power at a somewhat cheaper rate than conventional methods do. The reason for this is the possibility of direct conversion of the energy output of the system into electrical energy. As will be seen later in these lectures, the working fluid of a Sherwood device is a completely ionized plasma at a temperature of 100,000,000 deg. It may not be too difficult to find some means of separating the charges in the plasma (at least up to a potential difference equal to kT, which is 10^4 eV) and actually obtaining a d.c. potential which can be used directly. Alternative schemes could involve use of inductive action by expanding plasmas.

A second reason is the goad of competition. It is well known that the U.S.S.R. and the U.K. are working on such devices. If these devices are successful, they could prove an important economic, political, or psychological achievement. Hence, it of in the national interest not to fall behind in this field is research.

The last, but certainly not the least, of the list of advantages is the question of nuclear safety. A thermonuclear reactor is probably an extremely safe device since the total fuel in it at a given time is only enough to sustain the reaction for a few seconds and since there are no fission products such as occur in uranium reactors. Shielding will be somewhat more difficult since the

B

neutron flux is considerably greater at the same power level and since the average neutron energy is higher than in fission.

Tritium replacement in a D–T reactor

It will be seen in the next lecture that the D–T reaction is in principle the most promising reaction to use in a fusion device since it has the largest reaction cross section. Unfortunately, since tritium does not occur naturally, it can only be obtained in large quantities from nuclear reactors operating on the fission principle.

The coupling of a thermonuclear economy to a uranium economy is an undesirable prospect. Instead, one would prefer to use the reaction products of the D–T reaction to regenerate tritium in some way. A possible way to accomplish this is to make use of the neutrons which result from the D–T reaction by absorbing them in a lithium blanket. The n–α reaction in Li^6 yields a triton which can then be recovered by some chemical means and fed back into the system. Hence, the problem is one of neutron economy and perhaps of neutron multiplication.

The calculation below is indicative of the magnitude of the problem. If C is defined to be the fraction of neutrons which are converted into tritium in the device, Eq. (1.1) then gives the situation at steady state for no net triton gain or loss.

$$\left[n_D n_T (\sigma v)_{D-T} - \frac{n_D{}^2}{2} (\sigma v)_{D-D(\frac{1}{2})} \right]$$

$$= \left[\frac{n_D{}^2}{2} (\sigma v)_{D-D(\frac{1}{2})} + n_D n_T (\sigma v)_{D-T} \right] C \qquad (1.1)$$

The terms on the left-hand side represent first the loss of tritium by D–T reactions, and secondly the gain of tritons from the D–D reactions which are going on. The term in the brackets on the right-hand side represents the rate of neutron production in the device. Equation (1.1) may be solved for C as a function of the ratio of the concentration of tritium to that of deuterium and also as a function of the cross-sections for the D–T and D–D process.

$$C = \frac{(n_T/n_D)[(\sigma v)_{D-T}/(\sigma v)_{D-D}] - \frac{1}{4}}{(n_T/n_D)[(\sigma v)_{D-T}/(\sigma v)_{D-D}] + \frac{1}{4}} \qquad (1.2)$$

It will be seen shortly that the D–T cross-section is about 100 times the D–D cross section in the region of interest.

It may be seen from Table 1.4 that the percentage of neutrons which must be recovered is extremely high, even for a reactor which has a 50% mixture of tritium and deuterium.

TABLE 1.4. TRITIUM RECOVERY

C	%T	%D
0	0.25	99.75
0.60	1.0	99.0
0.78	2.0	98.0
0.995	50	50

Hence, in any D–T device it will be a very serious problem to conserve neutrons so as to be able to recycle the tritium. This is an important factor in the economics of the machine and in the design of the blankets, coils, and shielding. Consideration has been given to the use of beryllium in the blanket to take advantage of the multiplication resulting from the $(n, 2n)$ reaction. In fact, at least one proposed working thermonuclear device has the feature that it may actually succeed in being a tritium producer[2] —that is, more tritium will be produced than is burned up in the device. This is an additional factor which is favorable to the over-all economy of the device.

Critical size of deuterium

Of course, the simplest way to create a thermonuclear reactor is to assemble a critical mass of deuterium. By this we mean that enough deuterium has been assembled so that the radiant energy lost from the surface is less than or equal to that being produced by the thermonuclear reactions going on inside the deuterium

---

[2] L. SPITZER *et al.*, Problems of the Stellarator as a Useful Power Source, NYO–6047 (Aug. 1, 1954).

mass, even at room temperature. As a result this system will begin to heat up. As it heats up, the reaction cross section increases and one would expect the device to lift itself by its own boot-straps to a reasonable operating temperature.

An accurate calculation of this critical size would be quite involved. Instead, let us perform the following highly-simplified calculation. The steady-state energy balance between black-body radiation and energy production in an opaque isothermal sphere of deuterium of radius r and temperature T is:

$$4\pi r^2 \sigma T^4 = \tfrac{4}{3}\pi r^3 \frac{n^2}{2}(\sigma v)_{\text{D-D}}E \qquad (1.3)$$

The quantity E represents the energy release of about 14 MeV resulting from the burning of two deuterons. The atomic density is denoted by n and $(\sigma v)_{\text{D-D}}$ is the reaction rate for the D–D reaction. This equation may be solved for the radius r with the result

$$r = \frac{6\sigma T^4}{n^2(\sigma v)_{\text{D-D}}\,(14\ \text{MeV})} \qquad (1.4)$$

From the behavior of the D–D reaction rate with energy (see Chapter II, Table 2.1), it is readily recognized that $T^4/\sigma v$ has a *minimum* value in the neighborhood of $T = 10^8$ degrees absolute ($1\ \text{eV} = 1.16 \times 10^{4\circ}\text{K}$, hence $10^{8\circ}\text{K} \simeq 10\ \text{keV}$). With this assumed temperature and with an assumed *maximum* reasonable density of 10^{22} particles per cubic centimeter, the following radius is obtained:

$$r \geqslant \frac{(6)(6 \times 10^{-5})(10^{32})}{(10^{44})(10^{-18})(2 \times 10^{-5})} = 2 \times 10^7\ \text{cm} \qquad (1.5)$$

Hence, even at the most favorable conditions of temperature and density the final size is about one-tenth the radius of the moon.

Of course, the calculation sketched above is quite inconsistent. The actual temperature of the device would decrease radially outward and consideration must be paid to questions of internal pressure balance. Nevertheless, the astronomical sizes that were found would probably persist in a more careful analysis. Obviously such a system is impractical.

CHAPTER II

BASIC CONDITIONS REQUIRED FOR A FUSION REACTOR

THERE are some basic conditions which are required for any successful controlled fusion reactor. These may be deduced from a consideration of the nuclear and atomic cross sections which are relevant. The most significant, of course, are the total nuclear reaction cross sections themselves.

Reaction cross sections

The D–D and D–T cross sections are shown in Figs. 2.1 and

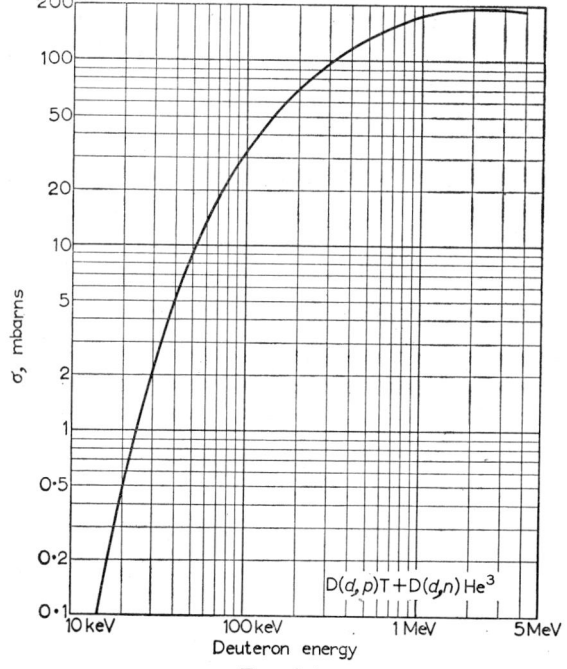

FIG. 2.1.

9

2.2. Since these are charged-particle reactions, the cross section is extremely small at low energies and rises rapidly as the barrier

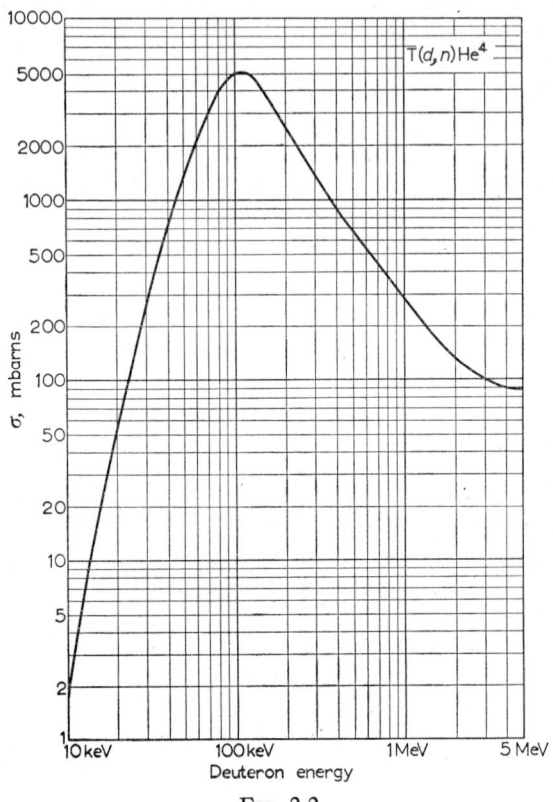

FIG. 2.2.

height is approached. At low energies the cross section is given by a Gamow factor of the usual form,

$$\sigma \sim \frac{A}{v^2} e^{-B/v}$$

where A and B are constants.

Note that there is virtually no energy production until the nuclei collide with energies of the order of 10 keV. Average energies of this order of magnitude occur in a gas at a temperature of about 100 million degrees. However, before considering the properties of such a gas, it is instructive to see why some simpler schemes fail and why these considerations always lead back to the hot gas (or plasma) concept.

Solid targets

The most obvious way of obtaining D–D reactions is to fire a beam of deuterons at an energy of 50 keV or greater into a target of solid deuterium. Nuclear reactions will certainly occur. However, the number of these is minute compared with the total number of deuterons which simply slow down in the target without reacting and which deliver their initial energy to the target electrons. This ratio may be estimated as follows:

The average energy which an ion will lose in a collision with a cold electron is of the order of the energy available in the center-of-mass system. This is

$$E_{\text{C.M.}} = \tfrac{1}{2}mv_{\text{ion}}^2$$

since the reduced mass is $mM/(m + M) \simeq m$ and the relative velocity is that of the ion alone (very cold electron, i.e. the electron *velocity* is small compared to the ion *velocity*). Hence

$$E_{\text{C.M.}} = \frac{1}{2}\frac{m}{M}Mv_{\text{ion}}^2 = \frac{m}{M}E_{\text{ion}} \qquad (2.1)$$

and only the fraction m/M of the ion energy will be lost.

The actual number of collisions is determined by the cross section for coulomb scattering of hot ions on cold electrons which is,

$$\sigma_c \sim \left(\frac{e^2}{mv_{\text{ion}}^2}\right)^2. \qquad (2.2)$$

Combining Eqs. (2.1) and (2.2), one has the following expression for the time rate of loss of energy by an ion,

$$\frac{\mathrm{d}E}{\mathrm{d}t} = n_e\sigma_c v_{\text{ion}}\frac{m}{M}E_{\text{ion}}$$

$$= n_e\left[\left(\frac{e^2}{mv_{\text{ion}}^2}\right)^2\frac{m}{M}\right]v_{\text{ion}}E_{\text{ion}}, \qquad (2.3)$$

where n_e is the electron density in the solid target. The quantity in the parenthesis represents an "effective cross section" for an ion losing an appreciable fraction of its incident energy.

The fraction of the ions which actually produce a nuclear reaction before slowing down is determined by the ratio of the nuclear reaction cross-section to the "effective energy loss cross-section". At 50 keV,

$$\sigma_{loss} = \left(\frac{e^2}{mv_{ion}^2}\right)^2 \frac{m}{M} = \left(\frac{e^2}{Mv_{ion}^2}\right)^2 \frac{M}{m}$$

$$= \left[\frac{(4.8 \times 10^{-10})^2}{10^5(1.6 \times 10^{-12})}\right]^2 (3600)$$

since $M/m \simeq 3600$, and this has the value

$$\sigma_{loss} \simeq 7.5 \times 10^{-21} \, cm^2.$$

The cross section for the D–D reaction at 50 keV is of the order of 10 millibarns. Hence the ratio of reactions to energy loss is:

$$R \simeq \frac{10^{-26}}{7.5 \times 10^{-21}} \simeq 10^{-6}.$$

About 10^6 ions will lose all of their energy by coulomb collisions before a nuclear reaction occurs. This return is far too small to compensate for the energy spent in accelerating the ions.

The estimate given above is actually too optimistic! The coulomb cross section used is that which is valid for large-angle scatterings. Actually, the ions lose energy even more rapidly by repeated small-angle collisions and this can be shown to raise the effective cross section by a factor of about 100. (See the following section on coulomb scattering.) Thus it is more like 10^8 ions which lose all their energy per reaction. Some improvement in this ratio can be obtained by going to higher energies. However, the energy gap·remains an enormous one.

How might we eliminate this energy loss to the electrons? It is obvious that if the electron temperature is increased so that the average energy of the electrons is close to that of the ions that this loss rate will drop off sharply. Unfortunately at this temperature ($\simeq$ 100 million degrees) the solid target is no longer a solid, or a liquid or even a simple gas. Instead, it is a gas of ions and free electrons, i.e. a plasma. Thus the problem becomes one of creating and maintaining a hot deuterium plasma.

Colliding beams (coulomb scattering)

Another possible way in which one might attempt to create useful thermonuclear reactions is by the collisions of beams of energetic deuterons. If now, for reasons of space-charge neutralization, these beams contain cold electrons, we are no better off than before. Suppose, however, that these electrons are either absent or hot. Is this, then, a feasible method? The answer is apparently no, for at least two reasons. The first reason is the competition between elastic coulomb scattering and the nuclear reaction process. As mentioned in the previous section, cumulative deflections due to small-angle scatterings are actually larger than those due to single large-angle scatterings. Let us derive an expression for this effect.

Consider a particle of charge $z_1 e$ and mass M which passes a scattering center of charge $z_2 e$ at an impact distance b. The particle feels a deflecting force of magnitude $z_1 z_2 e^2 / b^2$ for a time

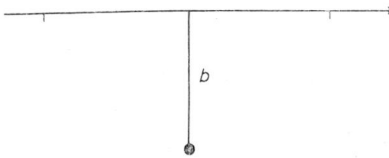

FIG. 2.3. Coulomb scattering.

of the order of $2b/v$. Hence, it suffers a momentum deflection of

$$\Delta(Mv) = \frac{z_1 z_2 e^2}{b^2} \frac{2b}{v} = \frac{2 z_1 z_2 e^2}{bv}$$

and a corresponding angular deflection

$$\Delta\theta = \frac{\Delta(Mv)}{Mv} = \frac{2 z_1 z_2 e^2}{bMv^2}.$$

This deflection angle is in the plane defined by the incident and scattered directions. If the particle passes through a gas of density

n, these deflections are in random directions and hence $\overline{\Delta\theta} = 0$. However, $\overline{(\Delta\theta)^2}$ is not zero and there is a random walk, in angle, away from the original entry direction. The total square deflection in a distance λ is directly proportional to the number of scatterings and is given by the expression

$$\overline{(\Delta\theta)^2} = \int_{b_{min}}^{b_{max}} n\lambda \left(\frac{2z_1z_2e^2}{bMv^2}\right)^2 2\pi b \, db.$$

The upper limit on b recognizes the fact that electrostatic shielding screens out the effect of charged particles beyond some maximum distance. This is usually taken to be of the order of the Debye radius (some investigators would argue for the inter-atomic distance) and has the value*

$$b_{max} = \sqrt{\frac{kT}{4\pi n e^2}}. \tag{2.4}$$

The lower limit is taken to be the classical distance of closest approach defined by,

$$\frac{e^2}{b_{min}} = \frac{Mv^2}{2}$$

or

$$b_{min} = \frac{2e^2}{Mv^2}. \tag{2.5}$$

(Actually the lower limit should be chosen to be either the classical distance of closest approach $2e^2/Mv^2$ or the de Broglie wave length $\hbar/Mv$, whichever is the larger. The ratio of these two quantities is the parameter $2e^2/\hbar v$ which is larger than unity until the deuteron energy is greater than about 200 keV.)

Now

$$\overline{(\Delta\theta)^2} = 8\pi n\lambda \left(\frac{z_1z_2e^2}{Mv^2}\right)^2 \ln\left(\frac{b_{max}}{b_{min}}\right). \tag{2.6}$$

Thus the mean free path for a random walk scattering through an angle of magnitude $\pi/2$ is

$$\lambda_{90 \, deg} = \frac{1}{8\pi n(z_1z_2e^2/Mv^2)^2 \ln(b_{max}/b_{min})}. \tag{2.7}$$

---

* This relation is derived in Chapter IX (see Eq. 9.12).

An "effective cross section" for a 90-deg deflection by means of multiple collisions can be defined in the usual manner

$$\lambda_{90\,\text{deg}} = \frac{1}{n\sigma_{90\,\text{deg}}}.$$

Hence

$$\sigma_{90\,\text{deg}} = 8\pi \left(\frac{z_1 z_2 e^2}{Mv^2} \right)^2 \ln\left(\frac{b_{\text{max}}}{b_{\text{min}}} \right). \tag{2.8}$$

It is found that

$$\ln\left(\frac{b_{\text{max}}}{b_{\text{min}}} \right) \simeq 10 \text{ or } 20 \tag{2.9}$$

for most conditions of interest.

The reader should be cautioned that this is not a cross section in the usual sense since there is not a linear relation between deflection angle and number of scattering centers but rather a square-root dependence. The quantity in Eq. (2.7) is a measure of the depth of penetration required for a multiple scattering through an angle of magnitude $\pi/2$. If a particle passes through a thickness which is 100 times greater, it does not suffer 100 deflections through 90 deg but only about ten of these. Nevertheless, Eq. (2.8) is a useful quantity in comparing the effects of coulomb and nuclear collisions.

The cross section for single coulomb scattering is readily obtained from the usual Rutherford formula. It is

$$\sigma \simeq \pi \left(\frac{z_1 z_2 e^2}{Mv^2} \right)^2.$$

Hence, the multiple scattering exceeds single scattering by the factor $8 \ln(b_{\text{max}}/b_{\text{min}})$.

An appropriate expression can now be obtained for the coulomb cross section at 50 keV. Equation (2.8) may be rewritten by the use of Eq. (2.9) as

$$\sigma_{90\,\text{deg}} \simeq 80\pi \left(\frac{e^2}{Mv^2} \right)^2. \tag{2.10}$$

At $E = 50$ keV, this becomes

$$\sigma = 80\pi \frac{(4.8 \times 10^{-10})^4}{[10^5 \times 1.6 \times 10^{-12}]^2}$$

or

$$\sigma \simeq 520 \text{ barns}.$$

The corresponding nuclear cross section as has already been seen is of the order of 0.01 barn. Hence, a 50 keV ion will be deflected through 90 deg hundreds of times before it makes a single nuclear collision. Once again the nuclear yield will be too low to compensate for the energy imparted to the accelerated ions, although by a considerably smaller margin. To narrow the gap one must somehow retain most of the scattered ions and cause them to collide repeatedly. In doing this, however, one has created a partially randomized gas of hot ions which is contained for some definite period. In other words, we are back to the problem of creating and controlling a hot deuterium plasma.

There is yet a second reason why colliding beams are an impractical means of producing useful power. This is due to the low particle density which one can obtain in practical cases. A typical beam density is, say, 10^8 to perhaps as high as 10^{10} ions per cubic centimeter. At this highest density the mean free path for a large-angle coulomb scattering (not to speak of a nuclear reaction) is

$$\lambda \cong \frac{1}{n\sigma_c} = \frac{1}{10^{10}\,520 \times 10^{-24}} = 2 \times 10^{11}\,\text{cm}$$

Thus, the beams will be entirely transparent to each other and essentially no reactions will occur. The solution to this, of course, is to keep the particles in each others' vicinity for relatively long times and this again brings us to the hot plasma condition.

Plasma radiation (ignition temperature)

Let us now concentrate our attention upon the properties of such a hot plasma of deuterons and electrons and consider what physical conditions must be attained in order that it be a successful power producer. So far, we have been speaking very loosely of a "hot" plasma without stating exactly what the minimum temperature must be. This minimum "ignition temperature" is actually determined by the radiation properties of the plasma.

Electromagnetic radiation is continually being produced in the plasma by virtue of collisions between electrons and ions. This is the well-known "bremsstrahlung". Similar radiation also occurs as a result of electron–electron and ion–ion collisions but to a lesser extent since the dipole radiation vanishes for these like particle collisions.

It is most important to recognize that any plasma which we can hope to contain must be entirely transparent to this radiation. The reason is because of the enormous radiation pressure which would result if the plasma were opaque. At even 1 keV, the black-body radiation pressure is:

$$P_{rad} = \frac{\sigma T^4}{c} = \frac{(5 \times 10^{-5})(10^7)^4}{3 \times 10^{10}} \text{dynes/cm}^2 = 10^7 \text{ atm.}$$

Hence, any realizable plasma will be transparent to this radiation and this loss will constitute a constant energy drain from the system. An expression for the specific power loss per unit volume may be derived in the following simplified manner: The power radiated by a dipole is given by the well-known expression

$$P = \frac{2}{3} \frac{e^2}{c^3} a^2 \tag{2.11}$$

where a is the acceleration of the charge. The radiation emitted in a coulomb scattering of an electron by an ion may be estimated by obtaining an expression for the average charge acceleration in such a collision. Consider an electron passing an ion at an impact parameter b as sketched in Fig. 2.4.

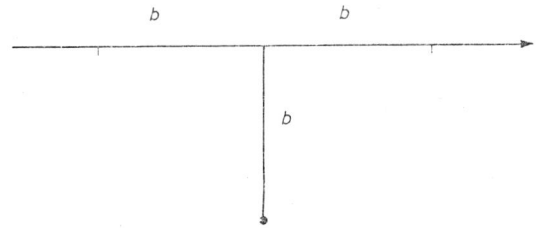

FIG. 2.4 Electron bremsstrahlung.

The coulomb force between the particles is approximately ze^2/b^2 and this acts for a time of the order of $2b/v$ where v is the velocity of the colliding particle. Hence, the energy radiated in a single collision at impact parameter b is

$$P \cong \frac{2}{3} \frac{e^2}{c^3} \left(\frac{ze^2}{mb^2} \right)^2 \frac{2b}{v} \, .$$

Summing over all impacts per unit time,

$$P = \frac{4}{3} \frac{e^2}{c^3} \frac{z^2 e^4}{m^2 v} nv \int_{b_{min}}^{\infty} \frac{1}{b^3} 2\pi b \, db$$

$$= \frac{8\pi}{3} \frac{e^2}{c^3} \frac{z^2 e^4}{m^2} n \frac{1}{b_{min}},$$

where n is the number of ions per unit volume. Now if there are n ions per unit volume, there will be zn electrons and the total power radiated per unit volume becomes

$$P = \frac{8\pi}{3} \frac{e^6 z^3 n^2}{c^3 m^2 b_{min}}.$$

The lower cutoff on the impact parameter is taken to be the de Broglie wave length $\hbar/mv$, since $e^2/\hbar v \ll 1$ for electron energies above about 13 eV. Hence

$$P \cong \frac{8\pi}{3} \frac{z^3 e^6 n^2}{mc^3 \hbar} \sqrt{\frac{8kT}{\pi m}}$$

A more exact derivation yields a slightly changed result.

$$P_{brems} = \frac{64}{3\sqrt{2\pi}} \frac{e^6 z^3 n^2}{mc^3 \hbar} \sqrt{\frac{kT}{m}} \text{ ergs/cc/sec.} \qquad (2.12)$$

It can be seen from this result that the power loss per unit volume due to bremsstrahlung varies as the square root of the electron temperature and as the square of the ion density. On the other hand, the nuclear energy yield also varies as the square of the ion density. The power developed per unit volume is

$$P_{nuc} \sim n^2 \overline{\sigma v}, \qquad (2.13)$$

where $\overline{\sigma v}$ represents the nuclear reaction rate averaged over the ion velocity distribution. This averaging is quite sensitive to the details of the ion distribution since the D–D and D–T cross sections vary so rapidly with energy. Assuming a Maxwell distribution of the ions, one obtains the averaged reaction rates given in Table 2.1.

TABLE 2.1. THERMONUCLEAR REACTION RATES[3]

kT (keV)	$\overline{\sigma v}_{\text{D-T}}$ (cm³/sec)	$\overline{\sigma v}_{\text{D-D}}$ (cm³/sec)
0.05	7×10^{-35}	2×10^{-35}
0.1	3×10^{-30}	4×10^{-31}
1.0	7×10^{-21}	2×10^{-22}
2.0	3×10^{-19}	5×10^{-21}
5.0	1.4×10^{-17}	
10	1.1×10^{-16}	8.6×10^{-19}
20	4.3×10^{-16}	3.6×10^{-18}
60	8.7×10^{-16}	1.6×10^{-17}
100	8.1×10^{-16}	3.0×10^{-17}

Note that the nuclear reaction rate rises quite steeply with increasing temperature, as expected.

The ignition temperature is defined as that value at which the nuclear power released in the form of charged particles becomes equal to the power lost due to bremsstrahlung. At this point, the plasma would continue to burn until it were consumed. Above this point, the plasma would heat itself up until some new balance was struck between loss and gain. Note that only the charged particles should be included in this accounting since neutrons will escape from the plasma instantly.

The ratio R of the power deposited to that lost is easily obtained from the previous calculations. Numerical values of R for the D–D reaction, assuming complete burning of the reaction products, are listed in Table 2.2. It is clear that a self-sustaining device will not be possible until a minimum temperature of about 10^8 degrees is achieved.

How can one hope to contain a plasma at 10^{8}°K? It is obvious that material walls will not succeed because they will probably

---

[3] These values are from a report by J. L. TUCK, Thermonuclear Reaction Rates, LAMS–1640 (March, 1954).

melt and during the melting or sputtering high z components will be added to the gas. As a result of the enormous bremsstrahlung ($\sim z^3$) which would result the gas would be quickly

TABLE 2.2

RATIO OF POWER DEPOSITED TO POWER RADIATED

$kT(\text{keV})$	$T(^\circ\text{K})$	R
1.0	1.16×10^7	0.00052
2.0	2.32×10^7	0.0092
10	1.16×10^8	0.71
20	2.32×10^8	2.1
60	6.96×10^8	5.4
100	1.16×10^9	7.8

cooled down and shut itself off. One's thoughts turn immediately to fields, and of these the only two which seem to be reasonable are electric and magnetic fields. It appears that electric fields will not be successful since a field which contains particles of one charge will not contain particles of the other type. A magnetic field seems to be the most obvious possibility, and in fact, the remainder of these lectures are essentially concerned with the problem of how to use a magnetic field to create a feasible controlled thermonuclear reactor.

Magnetic field and particle density and pressure

The general force equation for a plasma in a magnetic field may be written in the following form:

$$\rho \frac{d\mathbf{v}}{dt} + \nabla P = \mathbf{j} \times \mathbf{B} + \epsilon \mathbf{E} + \mathbf{F}_{\text{ext}}. \qquad (2.14)$$

Here all the properties refer to the averaged (or macroscopic) properties of the plasma. Thus $\mathbf{v}$ is the average mass velocity, P the pressure, ρ the density, $\mathbf{j}$ the current, $\mathbf{B}$ the magnetic field, ϵ the charge density, $\mathbf{E}$ the electric field, and $\mathbf{F}$ any other external force which may be imposed. Mixed Gaussian units are used throughout and no distinction is made between B and H since the dielectric (i.e. the plasma) is treated explicitly. This equation is exact except for the use of the pressure P. In the more general case, this would be replaced by a stress tensor.

In steady state, with no electric or external fields present, Eq. (2.14) reduces to the following form:

$$\nabla P = \mathbf{j} \times \mathbf{B}. \tag{2.15}$$

Now, by Maxwell's equation,

$$\text{curl } \mathbf{B} = 4\pi\mathbf{j}. \tag{2.16}$$

Substituting this in Eq. (2.15), there results

$$\nabla P = \frac{1}{4\pi} \text{ curl } \mathbf{B} \times \mathbf{B}$$

$$= \frac{1}{4\pi}\left[-\frac{\nabla B^2}{2} + (\mathbf{B}\cdot\nabla)\mathbf{B} \right]$$

or $\qquad \nabla\left(P + \frac{B^2}{8\pi}\right) = \frac{1}{4\pi}(\mathbf{B}\cdot\nabla)\mathbf{B}. \tag{2.17}$

In an uncurved field the term on the right-hand side vanishes and then

$$P + \frac{B^2}{8\pi} = \text{constant}. \tag{2.18}$$

If the gas is entirely contained by the magnetic field, the pressure drops to zero at the outside. Denoting the outside by the subscript zero and the center of the plasma by subscript i, Eq. (2.18) becomes

$$P_i + \frac{B_i^2}{8\pi} = \frac{B_0^2}{8\pi}$$

or $\qquad P_i = \frac{B_0^2}{8\pi} - \frac{B_i^2}{8\pi}. \tag{2.19}$

The maximum possible value of P_i which can be supported by an external magnetic field of strength B_0 is obtained by setting $B_i = 0$. Then

$$P_i^{\text{max}} = \frac{B_0^2}{8\pi}. \tag{2.20}$$

For the purposes of these lectures, a typical field strength of

c

20 kilogauss will be assumed. Some of the proposed Sherwood devices have larger fields (50 kG); however, at this point one begins to run into unusual problems of internal stress and fabrication. Assuming $B_0 = 20$ kG,

$$P_i \cong 15 \text{ atm.}$$

At a temperature of $10^8 °K$, this corresponds to a particle density

$$n \cong 10^{15} \text{ particles/cc.}$$

Thus, one will be dealing with a particle density which, even at its maximum value, would correspond normally to a good vacuum. However, the specific power production is anything but that for a vacuum. The value for a D–T system may be easily obtained,

$$P = \frac{n^2}{4} (\overline{\sigma v}) E$$

$$\cong (10^{15})^2 (10^{-16}) \frac{17.6}{4} (1.6 \times 10^{-13}) \text{ watts/cc}$$

$$\cong 70 \text{ watts/cc}$$

and turns out to be the usual order of magnitude found in conventional power plants.

It should be noted that in accordance with what has previously been discussed this system is entirely transparent to the bremsstrahlung radiation. The cross sections for scattering or absorption of γ-rays in the kilovolt region by electrons are of the order of the Thomson cross section ($\cong 10^{-24}$ cm²). Hence, since the electron density is 10^{15}, this corresponds to a mean free path of 10^9 cm.

Containment time

The final basic parameter which is needed is an estimate of a reasonable time scale. So far it has been seen that it is necessary to contain a hot random plasma in a magnetic field of about 20 kG with a maximum particle density of about 10^{15} cc⁻¹ and with an effective pressure of about 15 atm. How long must this system be held together? One would like to hold it long enough for most particles to undergo a nuclear reaction. This interval is the nuclear reaction time calculated as follows :

$$t = \frac{1}{n\overline{\sigma v}} \simeq \frac{1}{10^{15}\, 10^{-16}} = 10 \text{ sec, D–T}$$

$$\simeq \frac{1}{10^{15}\, 10^{-18}} = 1000 \text{ sec, D–D} \qquad (2.21)$$

However, the actual containment time need not be this long. Since the energy release per reaction is of the order of several MeV while the thermal energy is about 10 keV, one need burn only about one particle in a hundred "to make money", so to speak. A reasonable time that a system must be held together is perhaps given by the following two values :

$$t \simeq \tfrac{1}{10} \text{ sec, D–T}$$
$$\simeq 10 \text{ sec, D–D.} \qquad (2.22)$$

To sum up, then, the following typical conditions seem to be necessary for a controlled thermonuclear reactor.

$$kT \geqslant 10 \text{ keV}(T \geqq 10^{8}\,^{\circ}\text{K})$$
$$n \simeq 10^{15} \text{ cc}^{-1}$$
$$B \simeq 20 \text{ kilogauss} \qquad (2.23)$$
$$t \geqslant \tfrac{1}{10} \text{ sec, D–T}$$
$$\geqslant 10 \text{ sec, D–D}$$

CHAPTER III

SOME PROPERTIES OF A UNIFORM MAGNETIC FIELD

IN THE previous chapter we have calculated some of the basic plasma conditions which must be attained in a controlled thermonuclear reactor. In addition, it appeared that a magnetic field is a promising medium for use in containing the plasma. In this chapter consideration will be given to the motion of a gas of charged particles in a *uniform* magnetic field. Attention will be centered on the components of the motion in the plane perpendicular to the magnetic field. The motion in the field direction itself is unaffected by the presence of the magnetic field and will not be considered until the following chapter. Single-particle motions only are considered with no account being taken of plasma effects, i.e. the influence of one particle on another through induced electric or magnetic fields.

Particle orbits in a uniform field

The equation of motion of a charged particle in a uniform magnetic field, B, is given by Eq. (3.1), where F is any constant external force which may be applied to the particle.

$$m \frac{d\mathbf{v}}{dt} = \frac{e}{c} \mathbf{v} \times \mathbf{B} + \mathbf{F}_e \qquad (3.1)$$

It is clear that the motion in the field direction (z-axis) is the same as it would be in the absence of the magnetic field. In the x and y directions Eq. (3.1) takes the forms

$$m \frac{dv_x}{dt} = \frac{e}{c} v_y B + F_x \qquad (3.2a)$$

24

$$m \frac{dv_y}{dt} = \frac{-e}{c} v_x B + F_y \tag{3.2b}$$

One may eliminate v_y from these combined equations to obtain the following result:

$$\frac{d^2 v_x}{dt^2} = \omega \left(-\omega v_x + \frac{F_y}{m} \right) \tag{3.3}$$

where
$$\omega = \frac{eB}{mc} \tag{3.4}$$

In the absence of any external force Eq. (3.3) reduces to a linear homogeneous equation. The solution is periodic in time and the motion of the particle is in a closed circle with an angular frequency given by ω. The corresponding radius of the circle is then

$$r = \frac{v}{\omega} = \frac{mcv}{eB} \tag{3.5}$$

where $v = \sqrt{(v_x^2 + v_y^2)}$ is the magnitude of the velocity in the plane perpendicular to the field. It is useful to remember that a 20-kV deuteron has a radius of 0.23 cm in a magnetic field of 10^5 gauss.

In the presence of an external force, Eq. (3.3) is an inhomogeneous linear differential equation. The most general solution consists of the solutions of the homogeneous part of this equation plus any particular solution of the entire equation. The previous discussion has shown that the solution of the homogeneous terms is a periodic motion in a closed circle. A particular solution is then found immediately by assuming v_x to be a constant in time. The result is

$$v_x = v_x^{\text{periodic}} + \frac{F_y}{m\omega}$$

Similarly, one could have solved Eqs. (3.2) for v_y rather than v_x and proceeded as above. The result in this case is

$$v_y = v_y^{\text{periodic}} - \frac{F_x}{m\omega}$$

In vector notation, the over-all motion can be written as a circular motion superimposed on a uniform drift velocity v_D having the form:

$$\mathbf{v}_D = \frac{c\mathbf{F} \times \mathbf{B}}{eB^2} \qquad (3.6)$$

The resultant drift is at right angles to both the impressed force and the magnetic field direction. Note that electrons and ions will drift in opposite directions if the external force is independent of the charge (e.g. gravitational or centrifugal forces). However, an electric field will produce motion in the same direction for both particles. In this case $\mathbf{F} = e\mathbf{E}$ and then

$$v_D = \frac{c\mathbf{E} \times \mathbf{B}}{B^2} \qquad (3.7)$$

Figure 3.1 illustrates in a qualitative fashion the mechanism by which a particle drifts across a field at right angles to both the field and the applied force. Note that the particle speeds up

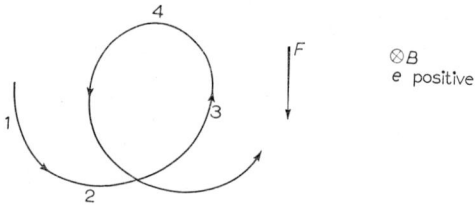

FIG. 3.1.

somewhat when moving in the direction of the applied force in region 1. This added velocity results in an increased radius of curvature of the particle in the magnetic field in region 2. In region 3, the particle is somewhat slowed by the applied force and has a smaller radius of curvature on the top swing (region 4). Hence a net walk results in the direction of $\mathbf{F} \times \mathbf{B}$.

Diffusion time across a magnetic field

The results of the previous paragraph have shown that in the absence of an external field and in the absence of collisions, a particle is completely confined by a magnetic field in a circular orbit. When collisions are taken into account, however, the particle begins to drift across the magnetic field by virtue of random collisions with other particles which shift its orbit in a discontinuous fashion whenever a collision occurs. The shift of the guiding center of a particle's orbit which results from a collision is illustrated in Fig. 3.2. Note that the maximum shift

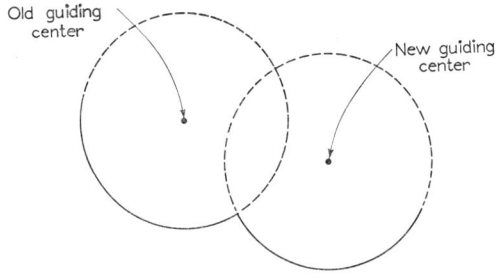

Old guiding center

New guiding center

FIG. 3.2.

which can occur is a distance $2r_0$, where r_0 is the Larmor radius. This collision drift is a purely random phenomenon; however, if the ion density is not uniform in space, there will be a net transport of particles from the region of high density to the regions of low density. The phenomenon is entirely analogous to ordinary diffusion and is proportional to the density gradient. The effective diffusion coefficient may be obtained by the following simple argument. A rigorous derivation is available[4] but the final result is the same. Those preferring a kinetic theory derivation will find this in Chapter IX. A derivation based on the plasma fluid equations is also in this last chapter.

The diffusion coefficient is equal to one-third the mean square shift of the guiding center per collision divided by the mean time between collisions. Since the average deflection of an ion in a collision with another ion is much greater than in a collision with an electron, one would expect the diffusion to be mainly by

[4] S. CHAPMAN and T. G. COWLING, *The Mathematical Theory of Non-Uniform Gases*, Cambridge University Press (1952).

ion–ion collisions. However, it can be shown (see Chapter IX and references 49 and 50) that like-particle collisions do not produce a net diffusion to first order in the density gradient. Under normal circumstances, then, it is the ion–electron collisions which produce diffusion across a magnetic field. Let us calculate this quantity.

The maximum deflection of an ion in a collision with an electron is readily apparent from the relation between the scattering angles of the ion in the laboratory and center-of-mass systems. This is shown in Fig. 3.3.

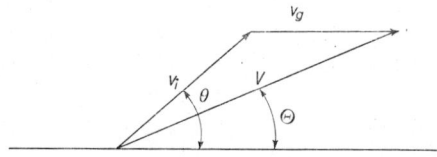

Fig. 3.3. Relation between lab and c.m. angles.

Here v_g is the velocity of the center-of-mass, v_i is the ion velocity in the c.m. system, θ is the c.m. scattering angle, and Θ the lab scattering angle. Now

$$v_i \sin \theta = V \sin \Theta$$
$$v_i \cos \theta + v_g = V \cos \Theta.$$

Hence, by eliminating V, one has

$$\tan \Theta = \frac{\sin \theta}{\cos \theta + v_g/v_i}.$$

Now

$$v_g = \frac{\left| M\mathbf{v}_i^0 + m\mathbf{v}_e^0 \right|}{M + m}$$

$$v_i = \left| \mathbf{v}_i^0 - \mathbf{v}_g \right| = \frac{m}{M + m} \left| \mathbf{v}_i^0 - \mathbf{v}_e^0 \right|$$

where $\mathbf{v}_i^0$ and $\mathbf{v}_e^0$ are the ion and electron velocities in the lab system. Hence

$$\tan \Theta = \frac{\sin \theta}{\cos \theta + \left| M\mathbf{v}_i^0 + m\mathbf{v}_e^0 \right| / m \left| \mathbf{v}_i^0 - \mathbf{v}_e^0 \right|}. \tag{3.8}$$

Let us assume that the ions and electrons are in thermal equilibrium. Then

$$Mv_i^{0^2} = mv_e^{0^2}$$

and
$$Mv_i^0 \gg mv_e^0$$
$$v_e^0 \gg v_i^0.$$

As a result, we can write Eq. (3.8) as

$$\tan \Theta \simeq \frac{\sin \theta}{\cos \theta + Mv_i^0/mv_e^0}$$

or
$$\tan \Theta \simeq \frac{\sin \theta}{\cos \theta + \sqrt{(M/m)}} .$$

Since $\sqrt{(M/m)}$ is a large number, we see that Θ is always a small angle whose maximum value is

$$\Theta_{\max} \simeq \sqrt{\frac{m}{M}}. \tag{3.9}$$

We have seen previously that the "effective cross section" for scattering of an ion through 90° by collision with other ions was given by the expression in Eq. (2.10). The result given in Eq. (3.9) tells us that the corresponding mean square angle of deflection in collisions with electrons is smaller by the factor m/M. Hence the mean square displacement is now

$$\overline{r^2} = r_0^2 \frac{m}{M}$$

where r_0 is the ion Larmor radius. Thus, the diffusion coefficient is:

$$D = \frac{\overline{r^2}}{3\tau} = \frac{r_0^2 m}{3M\tau} \tag{3.10}$$

where τ is the mean time between electron–ion collisions. The Larmor radius is given in Eq. (3.5), hence substituting this in Eq. (3.10) one obtains

$$D = \left(\frac{Mv_i^0 c}{eB}\right)^2 \frac{m}{3M\tau} = Mv_i^{0^2} \frac{mc^2}{3e^2 B^2 \tau}$$

$$\simeq mv_e^{0^2} \frac{mc^2}{3e^2 B^2 \tau} = \frac{\lambda v_e^0}{3} \frac{1}{(\omega\tau)^2} \tag{3.11}$$

where ω is the electron cyclotron frequency and we have used the fact that

$$\tau = \frac{\lambda}{v_e}.$$

The resulting expression for the particle flux due to diffusion is

$$nv_x = -\frac{D_0}{(\omega\tau)^2}\frac{dn}{dx} \tag{3.12}$$

where $D_0(=\lambda v_e/3)$ is the diffusion coefficient in the absence of a magnetic field. Finally, Eq. (3.12) can be written in a form which is valid even when $B = 0$ by a simple change, as follows:

$$nv_x = \frac{-D_0}{1 + (\omega\tau)^2}\frac{dn}{dx}. \tag{3.13}$$

Equation (3.13) is actually a precise result. In most applications however, in these lectures, the inclusion of the factor of unity in the denominator is a luxury since $(\omega\tau)^2$ is enormously greater than one.

Equation (3.13) may now be used to estimate the diffusion time of a particle across a magnetic field. This estimate will be based on the standard conditions listed at the end of Chapter II. First of all

$$\omega = \frac{eB}{mc} = \frac{(4.8 \times 10^{-10})(2 \times 10^4)}{(9.1 \times 10^{-28})(3 \times 10^{10})} = 3.5 \times 10^{11}\ \text{sec}^{-1},$$

since the standard field strength is 20 kg. Similarly, by use of Eq. (2.10),

$$\lambda = \frac{1}{n\sigma} = \frac{1}{10^{15}(5.8 \times 10^{-21})} = 1.7 \times 10^5\ \text{cm},$$

since $n = 10^{15}$ and $\sigma = 5800$ barns when $kT = 10$ keV $(E = \frac{3}{2}kT = 15$ keV$)$. Finally, the velocity of an electron at 10 keV is

$$v_e = 7.4 \times 10^9\ \text{cm/sec}.$$

Hence

$$\tau = \frac{\lambda}{v_e} = \frac{1.7 \times 10^5}{7.4 \times 10^9} = 2.3 \times 10^{-5}\ \text{sec}$$

and

$$\omega\tau = 8 \times 10^6.$$

This bears out the statement made above that $\omega\tau$ is usually very large compared to unity.

Assume now that a plasma is contained by a magnetic field in a cylinder of radius l and that the density falls off linearly from the center to the value zero at the edge. In this case $dn/dx \simeq n/l$ and Eq. (3.13) may be written as

$$nv_x \simeq \frac{\lambda v}{(\omega\tau)^2}\frac{n}{l}.$$

Hence

$$v_x = \frac{\lambda v}{(\omega\tau)^2 l} = \frac{(1.7 \times 10^5)(7.4 \times 10^9)}{(8 \times 10^6)^2 l}$$

$$\simeq \frac{20}{l} \text{ cm/sec.}$$

The diffusion time across the tube is then

$$t_D = \frac{l}{v_x} = \frac{l^2}{20} \text{ sec.}$$

It is clear that a tube of radius 50 cm would contain the particles for times of the order of 100 sec. This is entirely sufficient since the required burnup times are of the order of 0.1 to 10 sec. In addition, the diffusion time is proportional to B^2. Hence, a moderate increase in the field strength would rapidly improve the situation.

Thermal conductivity

The usual kinetic theory result for energy transfer by thermal conduction is

$$E = -K\frac{dT}{dx} \text{ ergs/cm}^2\text{/sec,} \tag{3.14}$$

where $K = \frac{1}{2}nk\lambda v$. In the presence of a magnetic field this result is modified in the same fashion as the diffusion coefficient. Equation (3.14) remains unchanged; however, the new definition of K is:

$$K = \frac{\frac{1}{2}nk\lambda v}{1 + (\omega\tau)^2}. \tag{3.15}$$

The rate of loss of energy per unit volume due to thermal conduction may be obtained by taking the space derivative of Eq. (3.14). The result is

$$P_{\text{cond}} = \frac{dE}{dx} = -K\frac{d^2T}{dx^2}. \tag{3.16}$$

Assume that the temperature falls parabolically from a central value T_c to a value T_0 at the outside wall, located a distance l from the center. Then

$$T = T_c - (T_c - T_0)\frac{x^2}{l^2}$$

and

$$\frac{d^2T}{dx^2} = -\frac{2(T_c - T_0)}{l^2}.$$

Inserting this expression in Eq. (3.16), the power loss due to conduction becomes:

$$P_{\text{cond}} = 2K\frac{(T_c - T_0)}{l^2}$$

$$= \frac{nk\lambda v(T_c - T_0)}{[1 + (\omega\tau)^2]l^2}.$$

There is one major difference between this calculation and the previous calculation of the diffusion rate. Although the contribution of ion–ion collisions to the diffusion rate vanishes in first order, this is *not* true in the case of thermal conduction. The ion–ion collisions are now the dominant factors in thermal conduction and it is the ion parameters which must be substituted in the above expression. For deuterium

$$\omega = \frac{eB}{Mc} = \frac{(4.8 \times 10^{-10})(2 \times 10^4)}{(3.4 \times 10^{-24})(3 \times 10^{10})} = 0.9 \times 10^8$$

and $v_i = 1.0 \times 10^8$ at 10 keV. Since λ is unchanged, we have

$$\tau_i = \frac{\lambda}{v_i} = \frac{1.7 \times 10^5}{1.0 \times 10^8} = 1.7 \times 10^{-3} \text{ sec},$$

and

$$\omega\tau = 1.6 \times 10^5,$$

which is still large compared to unity. The power lost per unit volume by conduction is

$$P_{cond} = \frac{(10^{15})(1.38 \times 10^{-16})(1.7 \times 10^5)(1.0 \times 10^8)(10^8)}{(1.6 \times 10^5)^2 l^2},$$

where it has been assumed that $T_c - T_0 \cong 10^8 °K$. The result is

$$P_{cond} = \frac{9.2 \times 10^9}{l^2} \text{ ergs/cc/sec.}$$

If a tube radius of 50 cm is assumed, the power lost by thermal conduction is of the order of 0.4 watts/cc. This is to be compared with a nuclear energy production of the order of 70 watts/cc, as derived in the previous chapter. It is clear that the thermal conduction can be much smaller than the nuclear energy generation and that the main mechanism of energy drain from the system will be by means of bremsstrahlung as has been assumed earlier.

From the results of this chapter, it would appear that a magnetic field is entirely satisfactory, both from the point of view of confinement of particles and from the point of view of conduction of heat, as far as transverse motion is concerned. The key problem—the effect of motion in the direction of the field lines—has not yet been discussed. In this direction, both the particle motion and heat transfer are unaffected by the presence of the field. This problem will be taken up in the next lecture.

CHAPTER IV

THE PROBLEM OF THE ENDS

THE MOST obvious way to reduce end losses is to build a very long
magnetic field. The required dimensions of such a solenoid are
determined in the first section of this chapter. A more subtle
approach is to wrap the field lines around into a closed toroidal
shape. This, too, has its problems and these will be discussed
in the second section.

Solenoid length

It is always possible to conceive of a solenoid which is so long
that leakage of particles and heat transfer to the ends become
negligible. An estimate of the required length is easily obtained.
It has been demonstrated that the diffusion and heat-transfer coefficients in the direction of the field lines are larger by a factor
of $(\omega\tau)^2$ than the corresponding coefficients at right-angles to the
field direction. Since the diffusion time and heat transfer losses
vary as l^2, it is clear that a solenoid whose length is larger than
its radius by a factor of $\omega\tau$ will have equal diffusion and heat
conduction losses in the two directions. Thus, the necessary
length L is

$$L \geqslant (\omega\tau)l$$
$$\geqslant 8 \times 10^6 l$$

Even if the tube radius is only 5 cm, which is only borderline
as far as containment time is concerned, the required length
becomes

$$L \geqslant 400 \text{ km}$$

Such dimensions seem outside the realm of feasible devices,
especially when it is realized that the volume must be highly
evacuated and filled with a 20 kG magnetic field.

The torus: Particle drift in an inhomogeneous field

The idea of eliminating the ends of a magnetic field by wrapping it into a torus is a rather obvious one and was first proposed in 1945 by Robert R. Wilson. At first glance, this trick appears to eliminate containment problems. The trouble is that the magnetic field in a toroidal geometry is necessarily nonuniform, as

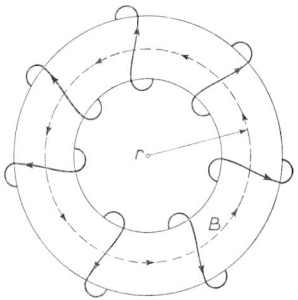

FIG. 4.1. Toroidal field produced by solenoidal windings.

is illustrated in Fig. 4.1. By Maxwell's equations, the integral of the curl H over the area contained inside the dotted line can be written as

$$\int (\nabla \times \mathbf{H}) \cdot d\mathbf{A} = \int 4\pi \mathbf{j} \cdot d\mathbf{A} = \oint \mathbf{H} \cdot d\mathbf{l}$$

The integral over $\mathbf{j} \cdot d\mathbf{A}$ is a constant for all dotted lines which lie inside the torus (conducting windings are on the outside). Hence

$$\oint \mathbf{H} \cdot d\mathbf{l} = 2\pi r H = \text{constant}$$

and $$H = \text{constant}/r \qquad (4.1)$$

Thus the field in a torus is nonuniform and falls off as the reciprocal power of the radius r. Unfortunately, a charged particle in a nonuniform magnetic field experiences a drift in a direction which is at right angles to both the field gradient and the field direction itself. Fermi called attention to the existence of this phenomenon (which had been known to astrophysicists for some time) immediately after Wilson's suggestion, and showed that the resultant drift rates were enormously faster than could be tolerated. To demonstrate this fact, it is necessary to derive an expression for the drift rate in an inhomogeneous field.

It will be assumed in this derivation that the magnetic field is entirely in the positive z-direction and varies in magnitude in the x-direction only. The equations of motion of a charged particle in the x–y plane take the form

$$m \frac{\mathrm{d}v_x}{\mathrm{d}t} = \frac{e}{c} v_y H(x) \tag{4.2a}$$

$$m \frac{\mathrm{d}v_y}{\mathrm{d}t} = - \frac{e}{c} v_x H(x) \tag{4.2b}$$

It is convenient to define a new coordinate s, defined by the relation

$$s = \int_0^t \frac{eH(x)}{mc} \, \mathrm{d}t \tag{4.3}$$

Note that x is an implicit function of t. Note further that the integral in Eq. (4.3) cannot be evaluated, in general, since to do so would require knowledge of the particle's orbit, which is as yet unknown. Nevertheless, this change of variable makes possible a series solution for the motion.

By means of Eq. (4.3), we may rewrite Eq. (4.2) as follows:

$$\frac{\mathrm{d}v_x}{\mathrm{d}s} = v_y \tag{4.4a}$$

$$\frac{\mathrm{d}v_y}{\mathrm{d}s} = -v_x \tag{4.4b}$$

These equations may be solved immediately to yield:

$$v_x = A \sin s + B \cos s \tag{4.5a}$$

$$v_y = A \cos s - B \sin s. \tag{4.5b}$$

The constants may be immediately identified as the initial values of the components of the velocity at $t = 0$. Thus, since when $t \equiv 0$, $s = 0$, one has

$$B = v_{x0}$$

$$A = v_{y0}.$$

Furthermore, by squaring and adding Eq. (4.5) it is clear that
$$v_x{}^2 + v_y{}^2 \equiv v_\perp{}^2 = A^2 + B^2 = v_{x0}{}^2 + v_{y0}{}^2 = v_{\perp 0}{}^2. \qquad (4.6)$$
Hence, the scalar velocity, or what amounts to the same thing, the energy, is a constant of the motion. This result is obvious since a magnetic field, for which the force is always at right angles to the particle velocity, can do no work on the particle.

Further progress can now be made by assuming that the magnetic field does not vary appreciably in magnitude in a distance of the order of the Larmor radius. In that case, it is permissible to expand the expression for the field strength in a power series in the field gradient,

$$H(x) = H(0) + \frac{dH}{dx}\bigg)_0 x + \cdots \qquad (4.7)$$

and keep only the lowest terms. By use of Eq. (4.7), Eq. (4.3) may be rewritten as

$$s \cong \frac{eH(0)}{mc} t + \frac{e}{mc} H'(0) \int_0^t x\, dt + \cdots \qquad (4.8)$$

The superscript prime on H denotes a spatial derivative of H.

Using Eq. (4.8), Eq. (4.5b) may be rewritten as

$$v_y = A \cos\left\{\frac{eH(0)}{mc} t + \frac{eH'(0)}{mc} \int_0^t x\, dt\right\}$$

$$- B \sin\left\{\frac{eH(0)}{mc} t + \frac{eH'(0)}{mc} \int_0^t x\, dt\right\} \qquad (4.9)$$

Now
$$\begin{cases} \sin[\theta + x] = \sin\theta + x\cos\theta + \cdots \\ \cos[\theta + x] = \cos\theta - x\sin\theta + \cdots \end{cases} \qquad (4.10)$$

where the omitted terms are of higher order in x. Hence Eq. (4.9) may be rewritten as:

$$v_y \cong A\left\{\cos\omega_0 t - \sin\omega_0 t\, (\omega_0)' \int_0^t x\, dt\right\}$$

$$- B\left\{\sin\omega_0 t + \cos\omega_0 t\, (\omega_0)' \int_0^t x\, dt\right\} \qquad (4.11)$$

D

where $\omega_0 = eH(0)/mc$ and $(\omega_0)'$ represents the same expression with $H(0)$ replaced by $H'(0)$.

For the expression to be evaluated consistently, the value of x used in the integral should be of zero order in an expansion in powers of the field gradients. This result is easily obtained from the *zero* order expansion of Eq. (4.5a). Thus

$$v_x \cong A \sin \omega_0 t + B \cos \omega_0 t$$

$$\therefore x = \int v_x \, dt = -\frac{A}{\omega_0} \cos \omega_0 t + \frac{B}{\omega_0} \sin \omega_0 t + c \qquad (4.12)$$

where c is the constant of integration. The origin of coordinates about which the field expansion has been made may always be chosen so that

$$x = -\frac{A}{\omega_0} \qquad \text{at} \qquad t = 0.$$

In this case $c = 0$ and

$$x = -\frac{A}{\omega_0} \cos \omega_0 t + \frac{B}{\omega_0} \sin \omega_0 t. \qquad (4.13)$$

Next,

$$\int_0^t x \, dt = -\frac{A}{\omega_0^2} \sin \omega_0 t - \frac{B}{\omega_0^2} \cos \omega_0 t + \frac{B}{\omega_0^2}. \qquad (4.14)$$

Substituting this expression in Eq. (4.11), one obtains

$$v_y = A \cos \omega_0 t - B \sin \omega_0 t + \frac{A^2}{\omega_0^2} (\omega_0)' \sin^2 \omega_0 t$$

$$+ \frac{B^2}{\omega_0^2} (\omega_0)' \cos^2 \omega_0 t + \frac{2AB}{\omega_0^2} (\omega_0)' \sin \omega_0 t \cos \omega_0 t$$

$$- \frac{AB}{\omega_0^2} (\omega_0)' \sin \omega_0 t - \frac{B^2}{\omega_0^2} (\omega_0)' \cos \omega_0 t. \qquad (4.15)$$

After averaging over time, the result becomes

$$\overline{v}_y = \frac{A^2 + B^2}{2\omega_0^2} (\omega_0)' \equiv \frac{v_\perp^2 mc}{2eH^2} \frac{dH}{dx}. \qquad (4.16)$$

In a similar fashion, the first-order result for v_x may be shown to be entirely periodic in time, and thus

$$\overline{v_x} = 0. \tag{4.17}$$

In vector terms, these two results may be written as

$$v_D = -\frac{mv_\perp^2 c}{2eH^3} \nabla H \times \mathbf{H}. \tag{4.18}$$

This proof may be pushed even further, although the details will not be given here, to show that no further drifts occur even if second derivatives of the field magnitude in the x- and y-directions are considered.

One final drift remains. The coordinate system has been chosen so that the z-axis is in the direction of the magnetic field. This implies that $dH/dz_0 \equiv 0$. However, the second derivative may not vanish and to be consistent with the results above, the possible influence of such a term must be considered. The effect of this term is found rather easily. The second derivative in z corresponds to a curvature of the magnetic field lines. A particle moving along a curved path experiences a centrifugal force which acts in every way as an actual external force does. An external force produces a net drift as has already been shown in Eq. (3.6). Thus,

$$F_{\text{centri}} = \frac{mv_\parallel^2}{R} \mathbf{r}, \tag{4.19}$$

where $\mathbf{r}$ is a unit vector directed outward from the center of curvature of the field. The radius of curvature is R and $v_\parallel$ is the particle velocity along the field lines. Substituting this expression in Eq. (3.6), one has

$$v_D = \frac{cmv_\parallel^2}{eH^2R} \mathbf{r} \times \mathbf{H}. \tag{4.20}$$

Equations (4.18) and (4.20) constitute the expression for the drift velocities of a particle in an inhomogeneous magnetic field.

Before applying these equations to the calculation of the drift velocities in a torus, it may be profitable to show that the drift

velocities just derived can be understood on the basis of a qualitative picture similar to that presented in Chapter III for the
drifts due to an external force. Consider a particle moving in an
inhomogeneous field as sketched in Fig. 4.2.

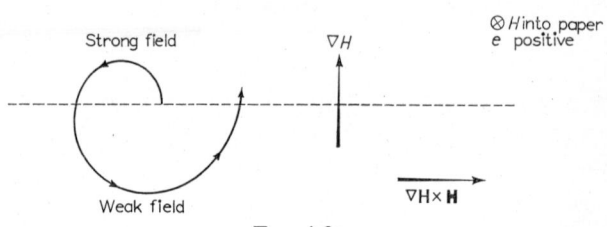

FIG. 4.2.

Note that the radius of curvature is smaller in the strong-field
region and larger in the weak-field region. The resultant drift
is obvious.

Immediate use may be made of these results to evaluate the
drift velocity in a torus. It has been demonstrated above that
$H = \alpha/R$ where α is a constant and R is measured from the
center of curvature of the torus. Hence

$$\nabla H = -\frac{\alpha}{R^2}\,\mathbf{r}$$

$$= -\frac{H}{R}\,\mathbf{r}.$$

Thus, by Eqs. (4.18) and (4.20),

$$v_D = \frac{(mv_\perp{}^2 + 2mv_\parallel{}^2)c}{2eH^2R}\,\mathbf{r} \times \mathbf{H}. \tag{4.21}$$

This result may be put in more convenient form by recalling
that for an isotropic gas $kT = mv_x{}^2 = mv_y{}^2 = mv_z{}^2$. Hence,
$mv_\perp{}^2 = 2kT$ and $mv_\parallel{}^2 = kT$. Thus

$$|v_D| = \frac{2ckT}{eHR} \tag{4.22}$$

Note that the direction of drift is up out of the plane of the torus for one sign of the charge and in the opposite direction for the other. The magnitude of the drift is readily estimated using the standard conditions.

$$v_D = \frac{2(3 \times 10^{10})(1.6 \times 10^{-12})(10^4)}{(4.8 \times 10^{-10})(2 \times 10^4)R}$$
$$= 10^8/R \text{ cm/sec.}$$

The drift time across the torus tube of radius r is then

$$t_D = \frac{rR}{10^8} \text{ sec.}$$

Assuming a tube radius of 100 cm, the drift time is

$$t_D = R \times 10^{-6} \text{ sec.}$$

Hence, it would require a torus having a radius of curvature of at least 1 km to obtain an average containment time of 0.1 sec. Such a device seems impractical.

It might be added that if one attempts to correct for the ∇H drift by the application of an electric field in the direction perpendicular to the plane of the torus, there is then a drift at right angles to **E** and **H** (see Eq. 3.7) which removes particles to the outside walls.

As a historical note, it might be mentioned that many of the results contained in these lectures up to this point were considered by a study group at Los Alamos in 1945 and 1946. Soon after the torus was shown to be impractical, however, further work on the subject ceased, apparently as a result of the return of most of the members of the group to the universities. Project Sherwood was born in 1951 as a result of two different suggestions for circumventing the containment problem which were contributed by Spitzer and Tuck. The details of these two proposals, as well as those of a third proposal made somewhat later by Post, will be presented in the next three lectures. Before turning to these, it may be interesting to consider some alternative proposals for achieving thermonuclear reactions which have arisen through the years and which have been uniformly unsuccessful.

Alternate schemes

(a) **Sparks.** A frequent proposal is that a gas be heated to thermonuclear temperatures by means of a high current transient discharge through it. The chief difficulties in this scheme are first, the inadequate containment time, and second, the fact that this type of heating raises the electron temperature quickly but not the deuterons. The energy transfer rate from the electrons to the ions is rather slow and the system disperses long before the deuteron temperature has risen appreciably.

(b) **Electrically exploded wires.** This proposal has all the difficulties of the preceding one. In addition, the addition of high z components to the gas results in a rapid cooling owing to the increased bremsstrahlung.

(c) **Mechanical shock heating.** Imploding charges and other such schemes will impart high velocities to the deuterons. However, when it is recognized that the thermal velocities corresponding to $10^8 °K$ are in the neighborhood of 10^8 cm/sec, it seems unlikely that such devices will be successful.

CHAPTER V

THE STELLARATOR

In 1951, Lyman Spitzer proposed[5] a means of avoiding the difficulties of the torus. The essential feature of his suggestion is that the torus be twisted once through an angle of 180 deg. The resultant geometry is that of a figure 8 or pretzel, as shown in Fig. 5.1. The advantage of this device (which has been given the name of "Stellarator") is that the ∇H drifts are in opposite directions in the two end loops. Hence it is conceivable that a particle which is moving around the device rapidly will have a net drift velocity which tends to zero. This suggestion has since blossomed into a large research effort located at Princeton University under the general direction of Spitzer and having the title of Project Matterhorn.

The actual devices constructed at Project Matterhorn up to this time have been relatively small in size and would require considerable scale-up before the theoretical nuclear energy output would begin to exceed the energy put into the system. However, a preliminary design study of a conceivable power-producer has been completed[6] and the device has been named the "Model D" Stellarator. The performance characteristics of a highly-simplified Stellarator will be analyzed in the first parts of this chapter. In order that numerical estimates be most meaningful, the relevant dimensions which will be used will be approximately those of the proposed Model-D device.

---

[5] L. SPITZER, A Proposed Stellarator, NYO–993 (PM–S–1) (July 23, 1951).

[6] L. SPITZER et al., Problems of the Stellarator as a Useful Power Source, NYO–6047 (Aug. 1, 1954).

Properties of an untilted Stellarator

It will be seen in the next section that there is some incentive for having an angle of twist of the Stellarator which is appreciably less than 180 deg. For the moment, however, it will be assumed that the angle is 180 deg and that the end loops lie in parallel planes. In that case, a top view of the device is shown in Fig. 5.1,

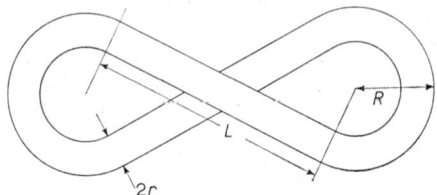

Fig. 5.1. Schematic of a Stellarator.

and a conceivable side view is given in Fig. 5.2.

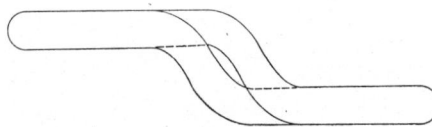

Fig. 5.2. Side view of a Stellarator.

The dimensions which will be assumed are listed as follows:

$$\begin{aligned}
L &= 50 \text{ meters} \\
R &= 8.5 \text{ meters} \\
r &= 65 \text{ cm} \\
H &= 30 \text{ kG} \\
kT &= 10 \text{ keV} \, (T \cong 10^8 \,^\circ\text{K})
\end{aligned} \qquad (5.1)$$

Gas Composition = 50% deuterium
50% tritium
Ion density at center $\cong 10^{15} \text{ cm}^{-3}$

The first point to note about the Stellarator is the fact that the particle drifts in the opposite end loops of the device do not cancel exactly. Hence, even if a particle does revolve around the tube rapidly enough so that it does not drift to the top in a single transit of an end loop, there will be a net unbalanced drift and the particle eventually escapes from the tube. The effect is illustrated in Fig. 5.3 where the dotted line represents the path

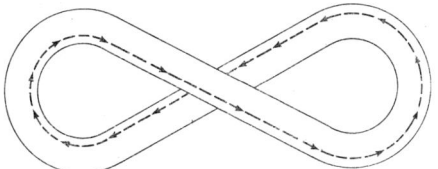

FIG. 5.3. Trace of a single magnetic line in the Stellarator.

of a particle moving along a single magnetic field line.

Note that if the particle is near the outside of one end loop it is then on the inside edge of the other loop. Although the drift velocities are the same in each loop, the time spent in the right-hand loop is larger than in the left-hand loop. Hence, a net drift occurs which may be calculated as follows:

If a particle has a velocity $v_{\parallel}$ along a field line in the Stellarator, it will spend a time t in the traversal of a single end loop given by

$$t = \frac{\pi \tilde{R}}{v_{\parallel}} \tag{5.2}$$

where $\tilde{R}$ is the radius of curvature of the field line in the end loop. (For simplicity, the subtended angle of the end loop is taken to be precisely π.) The total distance drifted in this time is then given by

$$\Delta x = v_D \frac{\pi \tilde{R}}{v_{\parallel}} \tag{5.3}$$

where v_D has the value given by Eq. (4.22). After a traversal of *both* end loops, the net distance of drift is now

$$\Delta x = v_D \frac{\pi \Delta \tilde{R}}{v_{\parallel}} \tag{5.4}$$

where $\Delta \tilde{R}$ is the difference in radii of curvature of the field line in the two end loops. The difference in radii of curvature is of the order of the vacuum tube radius. Hence, the average value of the net drift in a single revolution around the Stellarator is

$$\overline{\varDelta x} = v_D \frac{\pi r}{v_\parallel} \tag{5.5}$$

Finally, the time spent in a single revolution around the tube is

$$t_R = \frac{2(L + \pi R)}{v_\parallel}. \tag{5.6}$$

Hence the effective drift velocity becomes

$$\overline{v_D} = \frac{\overline{\varDelta x}}{t_R} = v_D \frac{\pi r}{2(L + \pi R)}. \tag{5.7}$$

The net effect of the figure 8 is to reduce the effective drift velocity by a geometrical factor which is easily calculated using the standard dimensions listed in Eq. (5.1). The result is

$$\overline{v_D} \simeq \frac{v_D}{75}. \tag{5.8}$$

The drift velocity, v_D, has already been calculated in the previous chapter (see paragraph following Eq. (4.22) for a field strength of 20 kG. Upon changing this to the value relevant to the "standard" field of 30 kG, this result becomes

$$v_D = \frac{6.7 \times 10^7}{R} \text{ cm/sec.} \tag{5.9}$$

The drift time across a *torus* with a radius of curvature equal to that of the end loops of the Stellarator would then be

$$t = \frac{r}{v_D} = \frac{(65)(850)}{6.7 \times 10^7} \simeq 0.83 \times 10^{-3} \text{ sec.} \tag{5.10}$$

The change to a figure 8 geometry results in an additional saving of a factor of 75, as was shown in Eq. (5.8). Hence, the average containment time in the untilted Stellarator is then of the order of

$$t_s = 75t \simeq 0.06 \text{ sec.} \tag{5.11}$$

This new containment time is a considerable improvement over previous estimates and is almost in the range required for a feasible gadget. However, it is uncomfortably small and it is of great interest to investigate ways of lengthening this period. A method of improving the containment is discussed further below and in the next section.

There is an extremely important point which the reader should be aware of. The time estimate above applies only to those particles which are revolving around the tube sufficiently fast so that they do not drift to the tube wall during a single passage through an end loop. If a particle has a velocity $v_\parallel$ around the Stellarator which is below some critical value, it will drift out of the tube at the end loops in a time of the order of one millisecond (see Eq. 5.10). Of course, all those particles having a $v_\parallel < v_\parallel^*$, (where $v_\parallel^*$ denotes the critical velocity) will be lost from the tube almost immediately after start-up. The resultant population in velocity space is then depleted in those particles having a $v_\parallel < v_\parallel^*$. This initial loss is not serious in itself. What is serious is the fact that there then exists a steady leak in *velocity space* by means of which particles may escape from the tube. Thus, even if a particle has a $v_\parallel$ which is initially sufficiently large for containment, it may suffer an elastic collision with another ion which results in a new $v_\parallel < v_\parallel^*$. This type of leak may be even more rapid than the loss rate due to unbalanced drifts in the end loop, and will be calculated immediately below.

A convenient representation of a particle's location in velocity space is shown in Fig. 5.4.

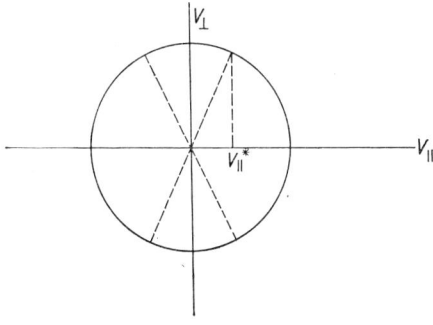

Fig. 5.4.

The diagram should really be thought of as three-dimensional. The abscissa represents the component of a particle's velocity in the direction of the tube axis. The ordinate, as well as a third axis at right angles to these two, represents the velocity components in the other two directions. Assuming all particles to have the same energy, it is clear that the resultant velocity vectors must lie on a spherical surface around the origin (represented by the circle in Fig. 5.4). The region of escape is then the annular surface within the dotted lines.

Assume that each particle has an average probability P of ending up in the escape annulus after a collision. Since the ion–ion collision rate in the gas is $(n^2/2)\sigma v$, the rate of loss of particles from the system by collision becomes:

$$\frac{dn}{dt} = -\frac{n^2}{2}\,\sigma v(2P) = -n^2\sigma vP. \tag{5.12}$$

Here n is the total ion density, v the ion velocity, and σ the "cross section" for elastic collision. The average containment time, t_c, resulting from this loss mechanism is then:

$$\frac{n}{t_c} \simeq n^2\sigma vP$$

or

$$t_c \simeq \frac{1}{n\sigma vP}. \tag{5.13}$$

The "cross section" which will be used in this estimate will be that corresponding to a 90 deg deflection as a result of small-angle scatterings. This number has already been derived in Chapter III (see discussion following Eq. 3.13) and has the value 5800 barns. Since $n = 10^{15}$ and $v \simeq 1.2 \times 10^8$, Eq. (5.13) becomes

$$t_c = \frac{0.14 \times 10^{-2}}{P} \text{ sec.} \tag{5.14}$$

Only the quantity P remains to be determined. Since the small-angle collisions are in random directions, it may be possible to estimate P crudely as the ratio of the area in the annular escape surface to the total area of the sphere. This ratio is

$$P = \frac{2\pi v \cdot 2v\theta}{4\pi v^2} = \theta,$$ (5.15)

where $\sin\theta = v_{\parallel}{}^*/v$. Now, $v_{\parallel}{}^*$ is fixed by the condition that the particles drift a distance of the order of the tube radius in one transit through an end loop. Hence

$$v_D \frac{\pi R}{v_{\parallel}{}^*} = r,$$

or by Eq. (4.22),
$$\frac{v_{\parallel}{}^*}{v} = \frac{v_D}{v}\frac{\pi R}{r} = \frac{2\pi ckT.}{eHvr}$$ (5.16)

By Eqs. (5.9) and (5.1), this quantity becomes

$$\frac{v_{\parallel}{}^*}{v} = \frac{\pi(6.7 \times 10^7)}{(1.2 \times 10^8)(65)} \cong \frac{1}{37}.$$

Hence, by Eq. (5.15)

$$P \cong 0.027$$

and
$$t_c \cong 0.05 \text{ sec.}$$ (5.17)

Comparison of Eqs. (5.11) and (5.17) shows that the loss of particles due to collision diffusion in velocity space is about the same as the loss rate due to uncompensated drifts in the end loops. Since one limiting factor on containment is the non-cancelling drifts, it will pay to investigate methods of improving this situation. A large improvement would clearly result if the particle could be made to rotate gradually around the tube axis while performing its revolution around the Stellarator. The terminology which is used here is that due to Spitzer. Revolution will denote motion around the Stellarator in the direction of the tube axis. Rotation will refer to a circular motion about the tube axis. If such a rotation did occur it is clear that the uncancelled drift in the end loops would gradually reverse its direction and tend to move the particle in the opposite direction. (It is assumed, of course, that the rotation rate is not so small that the particle will drift to the end walls before the drift direction has reversed.) There is still a net over-all drift away from the particle's original position, but it is now the result of a series of random walks, where each random walk is of the order of magnitude of the distance drifted before the direction reverses.

Assume now that the rotation rate has been adjusted to be *approximately* half the revolution rate, by some means as yet unspecified. This means that the particle approximately reverses its direction after a single revolution around the Stellarator. Hence, the individual random walks will be of the order of the net uncancelled drift resulting from a single revolution. This drift has already been calculated in Eq. (5.5). Denoting the individual walk by l, one has

$$l = v_D \frac{\pi r}{v_{\parallel}}. \tag{5.18}$$

The over-all drift, S, resulting from N revolutions around the Stellarator is then

$$S^2 = Nl^2. \tag{5.19}$$

Now, in a time t, the number of revolutions is

$$N = \frac{v_{\parallel} t}{2(L + \pi R)}. \tag{5.20}$$

Hence

$$S^2 \cong \frac{v_{\parallel} t}{2(L + \pi R)} \left(\frac{v_D \pi r}{v_{\parallel}}\right)^2,$$

and the effective containment time for random walk across the tube of radius r is

$$t_R = \frac{2(L + \pi R)}{v_{\parallel}} \left(\frac{v_{\parallel}}{\pi v_D}\right)^2, \tag{5.21}$$

This result is to be contrasted with the time required for drift across the tube in the absence of any rotation. In this case, by Eq. (5.7),

$$t = \frac{r}{v_D} = \frac{2(L + \pi R)}{\pi v_D}. \tag{5.22}$$

Hence, the containment time has been lengthened as a result of rotation by the factor

$$\frac{t_R}{t} = \frac{v_{\parallel}}{\pi v_D}, \tag{5.23}$$

which has the numerical value, by Eq. (5.9), of

$$\frac{t_R}{t} = \frac{(1.2 \times 10^8)(850)}{\pi(6.7 \times 10^7)} = 480. \tag{5.24}$$

The containment time in a Stellarator, without rotation, has been derived previously (Eq. 5.11) and shown to have the value 0.06 sec. Upon addition of a rotation as described above, the new containment time becomes:

$$t \simeq 29 \text{ sec.} \tag{5.25}$$

It is important to note that the actual containment time in the device under investigation is not 29 sec but rather 0.05 sec as was shown in Eq. (5.17). This loss rate is that due to collision diffusion in velocity space. That is, the loss resulting when a particle acquires a low value of $v_{\parallel}$ after a collision and drifts to the wall of an end loop in one transit of that loop. Previously this loss rate was about equal to the uncancelled drift rate which was 0.06 sec. The improvement by a factor of 480, due to rotation of the plasma, resulted in a new drift rate of 29 sec. Hence, the dominant factor is now the loss rate by collision diffusion in velocity space. A containment time of 0.05 sec is barely sufficient for a D–T reactor. Any improvement over this value would be very welcome, and in fact the section on "Scallops" below indicates the extent to which the value estimated in Eq. (5.17) may be improved.

A second point which is of importance is the fact that the rotation rate was chosen to be *approximately* half the revolution rate. It is clear that any smaller rotation rate would result in a faster drift. This is because there would be a longer uncancelled drift before the drift direction reversed. Hence, each random walk is longer and the net drift larger. Similarly, an appreciably faster rotation rate would destroy the correlation between a single transit of the two end loops. The advantage of the near-cancellation of the individual drifts in each end loop would be lost, and the random walk would now be of the order of the drift in a *single* end loop. This drift has the value $v_D \pi R / v_\parallel$ rather than the value $v_D \pi r / v_\parallel$ as given in Eq. (5.5). The resultant containment time would be reduced by the factor $2(R/r)^2$ which has the numerical value of 340. Hence, the new containment time would be only slightly better than the time in the absence of rotation, if the rotation rate is chosen too large.

To summarize, the discussion above has shown that the containment time resulting from random drifts may be greatly increased by imparting a rotation rate to the plasma which is approximately half the rate at which particles revolve around the Stellarator. The derivation above has been highly simplified and has ignored many important phenomena such as the effects of an exact integral relation between the particle's revolution and rotation rates. Spitzer has investigated these phenomena in detail[7] and the reader is referred to this report for further details.

Rotation and tilting

Although a rotation of the plasma has been shown to be desirable, no method of accomplishing this end has been mentioned so far. One obvious scheme for producing a rotation is to impose a radial electric field on the plasma. The resultant $\mathbf{E} \times \mathbf{H}$ drift is in the θ-direction with a velocity given by Eq. (3.7). Thus

$$v_\theta = \frac{cE}{H}.$$

Now, if the rotation rate is to be of the order of half the revolution rate,

$$\frac{v_\theta}{2\pi(r/2)} \cong \frac{1}{2} \frac{v_\parallel}{2(L + \pi R)}$$

---

[7] L. Spitzer, Particle Orbits in a Low-Density Stellarator, NYO–995 (PM–S–3) (Oct. 1, 1951).

Hence

$$v_\theta \cong \frac{\pi r}{4(L + \pi R)} \, v_{\parallel}.$$

Upon substitution of the standard dimensions, one has

$$v_\theta \cong \frac{\pi(65)(1.2 \times 10^8)}{4[50 + \pi(8.5)]10^2} \cong 0.8 \times 10^6 \, \text{cm/sec.}$$

Hence

$$E_r \cong \frac{(0.8 \times 10^6)(3 \times 10^4)}{3 \times 10^{10}} = 0.8 \, \text{esu}$$

or $$E_r \cong 240 \, \text{V/cm.} \tag{5.26}$$

While the necessary electric field is quite large, the magnitude itself is not a formidable difficulty since potential differences of the order of $kT (\cong 10^4 \, \text{eV})$ can be maintained in a plasma. The more essential difficulty is the fact that an electric field can not penetrate appreciably into the interior of a highly-ionized plasma. Most of the potential drop across a plasma occurs in a narrow "sheath" region near the surface and no field is felt in the interior. The sheath thickness should normally be of the dimensions of the Larmor radius of the ions, which is about 1 cm for the assumed conditions. Hence, no beneficial rotation may be produced in the interior by this technique.

There is a second method which will produce an effective rotation of the plasma. This method is to tilt the end loops relative to each other. If each end loop has been tilted through an angle ϕ relative to the original plane of the Stellarator, there will be an effective rotation of each magnetic line by the angle 4ϕ upon each complete revolution through the device. This effect is demonstrated in Figs. 5.5 and 5.6.

Consider the four cross sections of the Stellarator denoted by α, β, γ, and δ. If these are viewed end on, the resulting spatial relations are as shown in Fig. 5.6. Note that the plane of the γ–δ end loop is tilted through an angle ϕ to the horizontal and that the α–β end loop is tilted by the same angle in the opposite

E

direction. Consider a particle which starts out at the point
denoted by x in the α-plane. In moving around the end loop

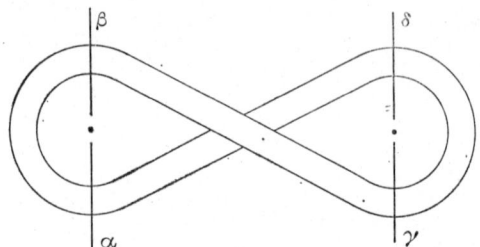

FIG. 5.5. Top view of the Stellarator.

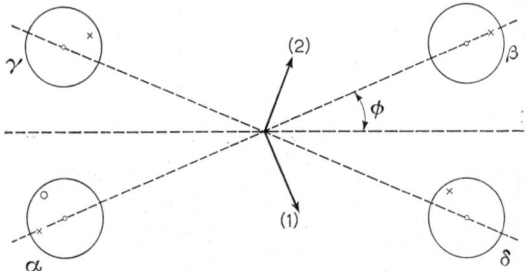

FIG. 5.6. End-on view of the Stellarator.

from α to β, the particle reaches the position denoted by the x
in the β-plane, and which is found by reflecting the diagram
about the axis denoted by (1) which is perpendicular to the
plane of the α–β end loop. Next, the particle moves from β to
γ by means of a straight section. Its relative position must be
exactly the same in the γ-plane as it was in the β-plane and this
is also shown by the x in the γ-plane in Fig. 5.6. The transition
from γ to δ occurs in the γ–δ end loop and is found by reflection
about axis (2) which is perpendicular to the γ–δ end loop. Finally,
the particle returns to the α-plane by means of the other straight
section and its second intersection is denoted by the open circle
in the diagram. It is clear that the particle has rotated through
some angle in the process. The formal proof in the next paragraph shows that this angle has the value 4ϕ.

Consider a vector which lies at an angle θ_0 from the x-axis, as illustrated in Fig. 5.7. Suppose that this vector is reflected

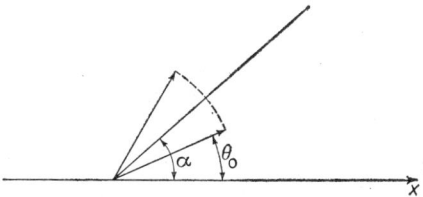

Fig. 5.7. Formal proof of rotation angle.

about an axis which is itself at an angle α relative to the x-axis. The new vector which results from this reflection is denoted by the dotted line in Fig. 5.7 and is clearly at the angle $2\alpha-\theta_0$ from the x-axis. The entire operation may be written, symbolically, as:

$$R_a[\exp(i\theta_0)] = \exp[i(2\alpha - \theta_0)], \qquad (5.27)$$

where R denotes the reflection operation. Now, if a second reflection about a second axis which is at an angle β occurs, the final vector is easily found.

$$R_\beta\{\exp[i(2\alpha - \theta_0)]\} = \exp[i(2\beta - 2\alpha + \theta_0)]. \qquad (5.28)$$

Hence, the initial vector has been rotated through an angle given by $2(\alpha-\beta)$ as a result of the two reflections. In the case of the Stellarator (see Fig. 5.6),

$$\alpha = \phi + \frac{\pi}{2}$$

$$\beta = \frac{\pi}{2} - \phi$$

and hence $\qquad 2(\alpha - \beta) = 4\phi.$

It has been shown above that the most desirable rotation rate would be approximately half the revolution rate. This implies that it would be advisable to choose $4\phi \simeq 180$ deg and hence $\phi \simeq 45$ deg. There are good reasons, however, why the angle of tilt should not be chosen as a simple integral divisor of 360 deg. Owing to inherent imperfections in the device, and to the influence of the solenoidal currents in one section upon the magnetic fields in another part of the Stellarator, it will not be true that a single magnetic line maintains the same radial position in the tube after a single revolution. However, it has just been shown that the motion of a magnetic line after each revolution is primarily rotational in nature. Kruskal has shown, in this case, that if it takes N traversals of the Stellarator to produce a return close to the original azimuthal angle, then the deviation in radius after this time is

$$\delta_r \sim e^{-N}$$

Hence, there is a strong incentive to choose an odd angle of tilt. The tilt chosen for Model D is stated to be about 40 deg, while that for a proposed smaller scale device known as Model C has been listed more precisely as 48 deg 15 min. In addition, there is an experimental model under design, Model A-2 (Etude), which will have a variable transform angle and which should provide an experimental test of some of these considerations.

Convection currents and "scallops"

There is an inherent difficulty in the Stellarator which was recognized by Spitzer quite early. All the particles in a given end loop have a simultaneous drift in the same direction, say the upward direction. The great majority of these particles do not strike the walls in the end loop, but rather proceed down both of the straight sections to the other end loop where they then drift in the downward direction. The result of these drifts is a convection current in the Stellarator in which the current in the upper part of the straight sections is in one direction and that in the lower part is in the opposite direction. This situation is sketched in Fig. 5.8. The arrows denote the direction of current flow. As a result of these convection currents there will

FIG. 5.8. Side view of a straight section.

be a magnetic field produced in the straight section which lies in the horizontal plane of the Stellarator and which points at right angles to the axis of the straight section.

The combined effect of this field due to the convection currents and the magnetic field due to the solenoidal windings is a resultant field which is no longer parallel to the axis of the straight section. Some of the magnetic lines will now strike the wall of the straight section. If only the outermost lines strike the wall, the situation will not be serious, since particles which have reached these outermost lines would have diffused to the walls in short order anyway. It is clear that there is some reasonable limit to the magnitude of the convection currents which must be invoked. This in turn implies a limit on the particle density in the Stellarator. This limit will be derived below by means of a very crude argument.

Let $\mathcal{J}$ denote the magnitude of the total current in the upper part of a straight section as well as that of the reversed current in the lower part. The resultant magnetic field at right angles to the straight section is then given by the approximate relation

$$H_\perp \cong 2 \cdot \left(\frac{2\mathcal{J}}{r} \right)$$

or
$$H_\perp \cong \frac{4\mathcal{J}}{r}, \tag{5.29}$$

where r is the tube radius. Now the total current moving along the upper part of any given straight section must be equal to half the total current drifting up in an end loop. This current, say $\mathcal{J}_{\text{LOOP}}$, is given by the expression

$$\mathcal{J}_{\text{LOOP}} \cong (\pi R)(2r)(2nev_D/c), \tag{5.30}$$

where R is the radius of curvature of the end loop, n the ion density, e the electron charge and v_D the drift velocity. Upon substituting the expression for the drift velocity given in Eq. (4.22), Eq. (5.30) becomes,

$$\mathcal{J}_{\text{LOOP}} \cong \frac{8\pi nkTr}{H}.$$

Hence
$$\mathcal{J} \cong \frac{4\pi nkTr}{H}.$$

and
$$H_\perp \cong \frac{16\pi nkT}{H}. \tag{5.31}$$

Now

$$P = 2nkT$$

since there are equal numbers of electrons and ions. Thus

$$\frac{H_\perp}{H} \cong \frac{8\pi P}{H^2}. \tag{5.32}$$

The ratio of the pressure in the center of a plasma to the magnetic pressure at the outside, $8\pi P/H^2$, is a very useful quantity in describing a plasma and is customarily denoted by β. With this definition, Eq. (5.32) may be rewritten as

$$\frac{H_\perp}{H} \cong \beta. \tag{5.33}$$

The ratio of $H_\perp$ to H represents the inclination of the resultant magnetic field to the field in the presence of distorting convection currents. The dependence of this ratio on β is in agreement with this interpretation since the distortion must vanish as the particle density, and hence the convection current tends toward zero.

Suppose now that a given magnetic line is in the center of the tube at the middle of a straight section. Owing to the distortion, this line will have moved toward the tube wall in the horizontal plane after traversing $\frac{1}{4}$ of the Stellarator, and the departure will be

$$\Delta r \cong \frac{L + \pi R}{2} \frac{H_\perp}{H}.$$

This departure is the maximum which will occur, since by symmetry the distortion will be in the opposite direction after the mid-point of the end loop. In order that the containment not be destroyed, it is clearly necessary that the maximum radial departure be small compared to the tube radius. Hence,

$$\frac{\Delta r}{r} = \frac{L + \pi R}{2r} \frac{H_\perp}{H} \ll 1$$

or

$$\beta \ll \frac{2r}{L + \pi R}.$$

A much more elegant calculation of this quantity was given by Spitzer[8] originally. He obtained the following result:

$$\beta \ll \frac{8r}{\pi(L + \pi R)}. \tag{5.34}$$

This limitation on the pressure is to be contrasted with that which follows from the diamagnetic conditions alone. By Eq. (2.19)

$$\beta = \frac{8\pi P_i}{H_0{}^2} = 1 - \left(\frac{H_i}{H_0}\right)^2 < 1. \tag{5.35}$$

On the other hand, inserting the standard values for the Stellarator from Eq. (5.1) into Eq. (5.34), one has

$$\beta \ll \frac{8(65)}{\pi[50 + \pi(8.5)]10^2} \simeq \frac{1}{50}.$$

Equation (5.34) represents a much more stringent condition on β than the simple diamagnetic condition given in Eq. (5.35). (Note that this condition is valid only for an uncurved magnetic field. It is possible for β to be somewhat larger than unity in a curved field.) The effect of a condition such as that of Eq. (5.34) upon the economics of the Stellarator is disastrous. For example, if the inequality is satisfied by choosing $\beta \simeq 10^{-3}$, the maximum particle density which can be achieved for a field of 30 kG is then $n \simeq 10^{12}$ cm^{-3} rather than 10^{15} for $\beta \simeq 1$. The specific power per unit volume is reduced by 10^6 and the resultant energy production is far too small to compensate for the resistive power

---

[8] L. SPITZER, Magnetic Fields and Particle Orbits in a High-Density Stellarator, NYO–997 (PM–S–4) (Jan. 28, 1952), Eq. (35).

put into the magnet coil windings. This point will be seen more clearly at the end of this chapter.

If hope is to be held out for the ultimate success of the Stellarator as an economical device, some way must be found to evade the limit on β set by Eq. (5.34). Spitzer has proposed a means of doing this by replacing the single end loop by a series of tube segments of alternating curvature. The resulting arrangement is sketched in Fig. 5.9 and has a scalloped appearance.

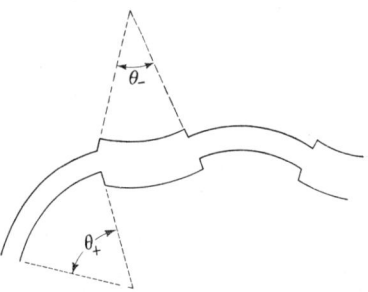

FIG. 5.9. End loop with scallops.

Hence, the name of "scallops" for this item. The essential point of this geometry is the fact that the drift currents in alternate sections are in opposite directions. Hence, if the total drift currents in each section can be made equal, the convective currents will tend to cancel within the end loops and only a small remnant will flow down the straight sections. This achievement will clearly remove the limit on β imposed by Eq. (5.34).

There is a second condition which must be satisfied. In order that the over-all geometry of the alternating sections be equivalent to the original end loop, it is necessary that the entire scalloped region turn through 180 degrees just as the end loop did. This can be accomplished by making the lengths of the sections of reversed or negative curvature (that is, with the center of curvature lying outside of the figure 8) smaller than the length of the sections of positive curvature. This condition can be made compatible with the requirement of equal total drift currents in each section. To see this, consider the following expression for the total drift current in a curved section having a radius of curvature R and having an included angle θ.

$$\mathcal{J} = \frac{ne}{c} \cdot \frac{2ckT}{eHR} \cdot 2r\theta R.$$

It is clear that the total current is proportional to the included angle, the pressure and the magnetic field as follows:

$$\mathcal{J} \sim \frac{P\theta}{H}.$$

Hence, if one wishes to keep $\mathcal{J}$ fixed and yet reduce the length of a section (which implies a reduction of θ) it is only necessary to reduce H in the same ratio. This may be accomplished by increasing the cross-sectional area of the regions of negative curvature, as shown in Fig. 5.9. Flux conservation insures that the field strength will be reduced in these regions. In practice, of course, the corners between the adjacent sections will be rounded off.

None of the present devices now in use or under construction at Princeton contain scallops. Hence, this innovation must be considered as an unproven item at present. It is clear that a great deal of experimental work can be undertaken without the inclusion of scallops. However, the ultimate economic success seems dependent upon the successful operation of this or some equivalent invention.

As a final word before leaving the subject of scallops, it is worth noting that the scallops will have an additional beneficial effect in that they tend to increase the containment time. It was shown earlier in this chapter that the limitation on particle containment was due to diffusion in velocity space and the resultant containment time had the numerical value of 0.05 sec (see Eq. 5.17). The key point in this estimate was the critical velocity for escape $v_{\parallel}^*$. This in turn was determined from the condition that the particle drifts to the end wall in a single transit of the end loop. With the inclusion of alternating sections of reversed curvature, this critical velocity should be much reduced since the particle's drift will reverse in a much shorter distance. In fact, if there are N scallops in each end loop, then the containment time should be increased by the factor N.

Present plans for Model D call for eight scallops in each end loop. This would lead to a containment time of about 0.4 sec. Unfortunately, this gain is partly offset by a more pessimistic calculation of the rate of diffusion in velocity space which has been reported by Judd, MacDonald, and Rosenbluth[9]. These authors took account of the loss of particles by assuming an appropriate boundary condition on the distribution in velocity space rather than by simply estimating the loss rate by the ratio of areas on a unit sphere, as was done earlier in this chapter. Although their calculations apply to diffusion loss in a mirror machine (see the next chapter) rather than in a Stellarator and hence cannot be used directly, the results did indicate that the more accurate assumption resulted in an enhanced diffusion rate. The increase in loss rate was by a factor of 2 or more. It is not clear to what extent this may affect the estimates of containment time for a Stellarator which were made above. In any event, it should be remembered that there are also some beneficial factors which have been ignored, especially the effect of sheath electric fields at the boundary of the plasma.

Injection and removal of fuel

The problem of injecting fresh fuel into the Stellarator is far from a trivial one. Individual charged particles cannot penetrate into the interior of the plasma because of the presence of the confining magnetic fields. It is clear that no pipe can be used to introduce the fresh material into the interior. Instead, thinking has been along the lines of injecting a high-velocity jet of liquid or gaseous fuel.

---

[9] D. Judd, W. M. MacDonald and M. N. Rosenbluth, End Leakage Losses from the Mirror Machine, published in *Conference on Thermonuclear Reactions, Livermore, California*, WASH–289 (June, 1955).

Calculations of the behavior of such schemes are quite preliminary as yet. However, it seems that any liquid jet is vaporized almost immediately as a result of the bombardment by the plasma. Furthermore, it will be ionized almost as quickly (microseconds) and would fail to penetrate into the plasma were it not for the possible action of cooperative electric fields in the plasma.

It appears that a blob of highly-conducting ionized gas which is moving with a velocity **v** across a magnetic field will have an internal electric field **E** which is produced by charge separation and which has just the proper magnitude so that the **E** × **B** drift (see Eq. 3.7) is equal to the velocity **v**. The situation is sketched in Fig. 5.10. Another way of seeing this is to note that

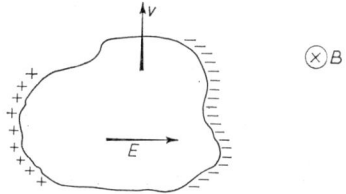

Fig. 5.10. Internal polarization of a moving blob of plasma.

the local electric field in a perfect conductor must be zero. In a moving frame, this field is given by the expression,

$$\mathbf{E}_{\mathrm{LOC}} = \mathbf{E} + \frac{\mathbf{v} \times \mathbf{B}}{c} = 0.$$

As a consequence of this internal electric field, the plasma blob is enabled to move across the magnetic field quite easily. Bostick[10] has performed a series of experiments involving the production and projection of plasma blobs across magnetic fields.

Owing to the finite conductivity of the plasma, there will be a drag on the plasma blob and it may be expected eventually to slow down and stop. The exact mechanisms of this action have not been investigated yet and deserve further theoretical study.

[10] W. H. BOSTICK, Experimental Study of Ionized Matter Projected Across a Magnetic Field, UCRL–4695 (May 10, 1956).

It is clear that part of the ultimate problem will be one of getting the blob into the interior of the plasma and yet not overshooting the mark. It is highly likely that the ultimate design will be based on thorough experimental tests.

A problem which has received more attention than the injection difficulty is the question of the removal of the hot gases and charged fission products which approach the walls. These ions must not be permitted to reach the wall for at least three reasons:

1. the heat to be conducted through the metal to the heat-transfer fluid behind it would be excessive;
2. the cooled ions would diffuse back into the discharge, tending to lower its temperature and stop the reaction;
3. sputtering of heavy metal ions or neutrals would result in increased bremsstrahlung with subsequent cooling of the discharge.

To avoid having ions actually reach the wall, a device known as a diverter has been proposed. The essential feature is that a thin shell of magnetic flux just inside the walls is brought out locally and spread out radially so as to provide a region in which the heat transfer can be safely accomplished. A sketch of the magnetic line configurations is shown in Fig. 5.11. Note that in the

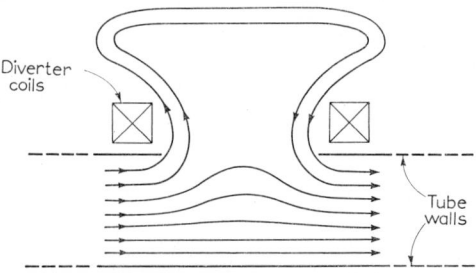

Fig. 5.11. Magnetic field in the diverter.

enlarged region, the flux density and hence the particle density can be greatly decreased. In addition sputtered and cooled particles can be pumped off more readily before finding their way back into the system.

A great deal of numerical work on the problem of the design of coil systems for possible diverters has been performed at Princeton. Recently a resistance analogue has been built which is capable of solving a variety of magnetic field problems in which there is axial symmetry. Up to the present time, only one diverter has been put into use. This item is on a device at Princeton called Model B-64. Preliminary evidence indicates that the diverter has a beneficial effect in that the electron temperature is maintained for longer periods and that the ion temperature may be considerably increased over its value in the absence of diverters.

Heating of a plasma

So far, nothing has been said about the method by which an initially-neutral, or slightly-ionized, gas will be heated up to thermonuclear temperatures. There are at least three methods which have been suggested and partially tested. Some or all of these will undoubtedly be incorporated in the proposed devices. Of course, it may be possible to begin by injecting a hot plasma since an organized particle energy of 20 keV or higher is not at all difficult to obtain. This possibility will be discussed in the later chapters.

All of the presently attractive methods of raising the temperature of a plasma involve inductive techniques, using either electric or magnetic fields. Methods involving the bombardment of a cold plasma with high-energy particles or X-rays appear to be quite inefficient. It is convenient to consider three stages of development in the heating of the gas. The first stage is the initial breakdown of the gas which provides a sufficient number of electrons for further ionization. The second stage is the attainment of complete ionization. The final stage would then be the heating of a fully-ionized plasma to thermonuclear temperatures. It will be seen that different schemes are more useful in each region.

The inductive methods which have been proposed fall into two general classes. In the first class, the electric field is applied parallel to the confining magnetic field. In the second class, the electric field is at right angles to the magnetic field. Two of the three schemes which are in use at Princeton fall into the first class. These are r.f. heating and d.c. (or Ohmic) heating. The third method is known as Magnetic Pumping and is a member of the second class. These methods will be discussed below.

r.f. heating. The application of a radio frequency electric field parallel to the magnetic field results in a very effective partial ionization of a neutral gas. Furthermore, an experimental setup of this sort is relatively easy to construct and install. However, effective heating depends upon the establishment of very high currents in the plasma. Such currents will be limited by the self-inductance of the plasma. Hence, after the initial breakdown of the gas, it will be more efficient to shift to a low-frequency (i.e. d.c.) heating scheme.

It should be noted that the energy is fed to the electrons by the r.f. field and is then transferred to the gas by means of collisions between electrons and neutral atoms. It should also be noted that the magnetic field has no direct influence on this type of heating since the particle motion in the direction of the field lines is unaffected by the field.

d.c. or ohmic heating. A low-frequency heating pulse can be applied parallel to the magnetic field of the Stellarator by making the Stellarator act as the secondary winding of a transformer. The primary winding is laid along the Stellarator tube and is energized by the discharge of a condenser bank through it. As in the case of r.f. heating, the energy is mainly delivered to the electrons directly. This may be understood quite readily by recognizing that the rate of energy input to a charged particle moving with a velocity v and under a force eE is

$$P_{in} = eEv. \qquad (5.36)$$

Since the electrons have a much larger thermal velocity than the ions to begin with, they gain energy from the field much more rapidly, further increasing the discrepancy.

An electron is continuously accelerated by the electric field until it makes a collision either with an ion or a neutral atom, at which time part of its energy is transferred to the target particle. If the rate of energy input from the field is slow compared to the rate of loss of energy by collisions, the process is entirely analogous to ordinary ohmic heating. Furthermore, the distribution of electron velocities may be expected to be very close to a Maxwellian form corresponding to the temperature of the electrons. On the other hand, if the electric fields are large enough that the electron gains more energy from the field between collisions than it loses in an average collision, a situation known as Electron Runaway will occur. The Maxwell distribution of velocities will no longer be even approximately valid and the electron energy will increase sharply until the balance of energy gain and loss is restored by some other loss mechanism (such as the electron striking the wall of the Stellarator).

A crude calculation of the threshold value of the electric field which might cause this condition can be made by equating the energy loss and gain rates. Thus,

$$eEv \cong n_i \sigma v \epsilon, \tag{5.37}$$

where the left side represents the rate of gain of energy by the particle having a velocity v from the electric field E. The right side represents the loss rate with n_i the target particle density, σ the cross section for collision and ϵ the energy of the electron. Now, in an ionized plasma, the cross section σ is that for coulomb scattering of an electron on an ion and is proportional to the inverse square power of the electron energy. Hence, it is clear that runaway can occur since the loss rate due to this mechanism decreases with energy while the energy gain rate increases. Solving for E, Eq. (5.37) may be written as

$$E \sim \frac{n_i}{kT}, \tag{5.38}$$

or

$$kT_{\text{crit}} \sim \frac{n_i}{E}. \tag{5.39}$$

Thus there is a critical energy at which electron runaway can occur. This energy is directly proportional to the ion density and varies inversely as the electric field strength. High-energy X-rays which are believed to be due to runaway electrons striking the wall of the tube have been observed on the Model B-1 device.

Berger and co-workers[11, 12] have made a careful theoretical analysis of the time behavior of an initially-cold plasma under the action of a constant electric field. It was found that an electric field of 0.045 V/cm applied for two milliseconds in a device of the size of Model B-2 could produce a completely-ionized plasma with an electron temperature of the order of 100 eV and an ion temperature of the order of 30 eV. Experimental observations have partially supported these theoretical predictions.

The numerical example cited above illustrates one of the major difficulties associated with class 1 type of heating. The trouble is that the energy is delivered mainly to the electrons. The transfer of energy to the ions by coulomb collisions is a very slow process. Hence, the ion temperature lags behind that of the electrons. Furthermore, the equipartition rate falls off as the temperature rises. Thus

$$\text{Part} \cdot \text{Rate} \sim n\sigma v \sim \frac{1}{T^{3/2}}. \tag{5.40}$$

It appears from numerical calculations that d.c. heating will never succeed in raising the electron temperature much above 10^6 deg.

There is a second difficulty in the class 1 schemes. The ohmic heating is inversely proportional to the conductivity. This last quantity increases as $T^{3/2}$ and hence decreases the efficiency of heating as the temperature is raised. Thus one must look for a new method for raising the ion temperature to thermonuclear values.

---

[11] J. M. BERGER and E. A. FRIEMAN, On the Pulse Method of Ionization and Heating of a Plasma, NYO–6043 (PM–S–10) (Oct. 7, 1953).

[12] J. M. BERGER et al., On the Ohmic Heating of a Helium Plasma, NYO–7311 (PM–S–21) (June 20, 1956).

Magnetic pumping. In magnetic pumping, heating is caused by a radio frequency oscillation of the confining magnetic field in a short section of the Stellarator. These short sections are called bulges since they are regions of larger cross section than the Stellarator tube itself. Of course, the flux remains constant so that the magnetic field is proportionately smaller. Auxiliary coils around the bulge will be connected to an r.f. oscillator and will produce a time variation in the field whose magnitude is an appreciable percentage of the magnitude of the time independent field. The varying magnetic fields produce circular electric fields in the plasma which are at right angles to the confining magnetic field; hence, the reason for this method being identified as of class 2.

There are several ways of seeing the mechanism involved in the heating process. They all are equivalent, of course. For example, from the individual particle point of view, an oscillatory field produces a corresponding oscillation in the radius of gyration of the charged particle in the magnetic field. A corresponding although reversed cycle, is exhibited by the particle's component of velocity in the plane perpendicular to the field. To see this, it should be recognized that the particle's angular momentum will be an adiabatic invariant in time if the magnetic field frequency is small compared to the Larmor frequency $\omega = eH/mc$. This is almost always so and hence one can write

$$mv_\perp r = \text{constant}, \tag{5.41}$$

where r is the radius of the orbit, m the particle mass, and $v_\perp$ the velocity in the plane perpendicular to the magnetic field. The Larmor radius is related to the magnetic field strength, B, by:

$$r = \frac{mv_\perp c}{eB}. \tag{5.42}$$

Hence, by Eqs. (5.41) and (5.42)

$$\frac{mv_\perp^2}{B} = \text{constant}. \tag{5.43}$$

F

Thus the transverse energy of the particle oscillates with the field. Substituting for $v_\perp$ from Eq. (5.43) in Eq. (5.42) yields

$$r \sim \frac{1}{\sqrt{B}}. \qquad (5.44)$$

This verifies the statement that the radius shrinks as the field expands.

An alternative way of seeing this result is to introduce explicitly the effect of the electric fields. By Maxwell's equations, the electric field induced around the particle's orbit is given by the relation

$$2\pi r E_\perp = -\frac{\pi r^2}{c} \frac{dB}{dt}. \qquad (5.45)$$

The combined action of the crossed electric and magnetic fields is a drift velocity in the radial direction as follows from Eq. (3.7). Hence, by use of Eqs. (3.7) and (5.45),

$$v_r = \frac{dr}{dt} = \frac{cE_\perp}{B} = -\frac{r}{2B} \frac{dB}{dt}. \qquad (5.46)$$

This may be rewritten as

$$\frac{dr}{r} = -\frac{dB}{2B},$$

which integrates to

$$\ln r = -\ln\sqrt{B} + \text{constant}$$

or

$$r \sim \frac{1}{\sqrt{B}}.$$

Yet another point of view is the magneto-hydrodynamic or fluid approach. The plasma is a highly-conducting fluid which tends to stick to the lines of magnetic flux. As the field oscillates, the magnetic lines alternately crowd in and then spread out. The plasma, since it sticks to the flux lines, is then alternately squeezed and expanded in the transverse direction. By flux conservation it is clear that the product of the radius of the plasma squared times the field strength must remain constant.

If there were no collisions in the plasma, or loss of particles from the bulge regions, there would be no net energy transferred to the plasma. However, owing to collisions, some energy will be fed into the longitudinal velocities of the particles. Furthermore, particles with altered transverse velocities will be escaping from the bulge region. Simple thermodynamic arguments assure us that these processes result in a net heating of the gas. The following simple illustration, due to Spitzer, indicates the rate at which the heating occurs.

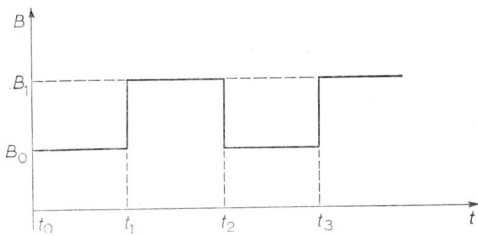

FIG. 5.12. Field variation in the bulge.

Consider a square wave variation of the magnetic field in time as shown in Fig. 5.12. The field has a value B_0 at $t = 0$. It then rises to the value B_1 at $t = t_1$. The ratio of B_1 to B_0 will be denoted by α. Thus

$$B_1 = \alpha B_0. \tag{5.47}$$

Assume that the frequency of the variation is slow enough that equipartition of kinetic energy occurs among the three kinetic modes of the particle. The resultant distribution of energies is indicated in Table 5.1. where E_0 denotes the initial total kinetic energy of the particle. The kinetic energy in the two modes transverse to the magnetic field is denoted by $E_\perp$ and that in the longitudinal mode by $E_\parallel$. At $t = t_1$ the field rises to B_1 and the transverse energy increases by the factor α as follows from Eqs. (5.17) and (5.43). During the interval between t_1 and t_2, this energy is distributed equally again among the three modes. Finally, at $t = t_2$ the field decreases and energy is lost from the transverse modes again.

TABLE 5.1. ENERGY DISTRIBUTION IN KINETIC MODES

Time	B	$E_\perp$	$E_\parallel$	E_{Total}
$t_0 < t < t_1$	B_0	$\frac{2}{3}E_0$	$\frac{1}{3}E_0$	E_0
$t = t_1$	$B_0 \to B_1$	$\frac{2\alpha}{3}E_0$	$\frac{1}{3}E_0$	$\left(\frac{2\alpha}{3}+\frac{1}{3}\right)E_0$
$t_1 < t < t_2$	B_1	$\frac{2}{3}\left(\frac{2\alpha}{3}+\frac{1}{3}\right)E_0$	$\frac{1}{3}\left(\frac{2\alpha}{3}+\frac{1}{3}\right)E_0$	$\left(\frac{2\alpha}{3}+\frac{1}{3}\right)E_0$
$t = t_2$	$B_1 \to B_0$	$\frac{2}{3\alpha}\left(\frac{2\alpha}{3}+\frac{1}{3}\right)E_0$		$\left(\frac{5}{9}+\frac{2}{9}\alpha+\frac{2}{9\alpha}\right)E_0$
$t_2 < t < t_3$	B_0	$\frac{2}{3}\left(\frac{5}{9}+\frac{2}{9}\alpha+\frac{2}{9\alpha}\right)E_0$	$\frac{1}{3}\left(\frac{5}{9}+\frac{2}{9}\alpha+\frac{2}{9\alpha}\right)E_0$	$\left(\frac{5}{9}+\frac{2}{9}\alpha+\frac{2}{9\alpha}\right)E_0$

The over-all gain in energy per particle per cycle of the field is seen to be

$$\Delta E = \left(\frac{5}{9} + \frac{2\alpha}{9} + \frac{2}{9\alpha}\right)E_0 - E_0$$

$$= \frac{2}{9\alpha}(1 - 2\alpha + \alpha^2)E_0$$

$$= \frac{2(\alpha - 1)^2}{9\alpha}E_0.$$

Hence, the fractional energy gain is

$$\frac{\Delta E}{E_0} = \frac{2}{9\alpha}(\alpha - 1)^2. \tag{5.48}$$

Now by Eq. (5.47),

$$\Delta B = B_1 - B_0 = (\alpha - 1)B_0.$$

Hence, Eq. (5.48) may be rewritten as,

$$\frac{\Delta E}{E_0} = \frac{2}{9}\frac{(\Delta B)^2}{B_1 B_0}, \tag{5.49}$$

and if the field variation is small compared to the field itself

$$\frac{\Delta E}{E_0} \simeq \frac{2}{9}\left(\frac{\Delta B}{B}\right)^2. \tag{5.50}$$

Finally, since this is the energy change per cycle, one can write a derivative relation

$$\frac{1}{E}\frac{dE}{dt} \simeq \frac{2}{9}\left(\frac{\Delta B}{B}\right)^2 f \tag{5.51}$$

where f is the frequency of field oscillation. Upon integration, this becomes

$$E \sim E_0 e^{t/T}, \tag{5.52}$$

where the e-folding time T is,

$$T = \frac{1}{\frac{2}{9}(\Delta B/B)^2 f}. \tag{5.53}$$

It is possible to obtain a crude estimate of the time required for heating a plasma by magnetic pumping to thermonuclear temperatures by use of Eq. (5.52). For example, if the plasma must be raised from 100 V (which temperature has been attained by d.c. and r.f. heating) to 20 keV, the time required is:

$$t = T \ln \frac{2 \times 10^4}{10^2}$$

$$= \frac{5.3}{[\frac{2}{9}(\varDelta B/B)^2 f]}.$$

For a 10 kc frequency, with the field varying by $\frac{1}{2}$ of the average value, the time for heating of the gas in the bulge is of the order of 10 msec. The time for heating the entire gas in a Stellarator might be expected to be much longer, in the ratio of the Stellarator length to the total length of the bulges.

It should be recognized that the estimates made above are exceedingly crude. In the actual situation, the field variation will be sinusoidal rather than as a square wave. More importantly, it will not be true in most cases that the equipartition time is short compared to the oscillation time of the field. Furthermore, the additional heating due to gain or loss of particles from the bulge region during the oscillation cycle must be included. These effects have been analyzed in detail by Berger and Newcomb[13] and the reader is referred to this report for further information.

Before leaving the subject of heating, it should be pointed out that magnetic pumping possesses a great advantage over the r.f. and d.c. methods in that the ions are heated directly and need not depend on interactions with the electrons to reach a working temperature. A possible peril of this technique is the introduction of plasma instabilities upon the squeezing of the plasma by curved magnetic fields. This point will be mentioned in Chapter VIII. Finally, magnetic pumping is not efficient for a weakly-ionized and cold gas; hence, the initial heating in the proposed devices will be by r.f. and then ohmic methods.

---

[13] J. M. Berger and W. A. Newcomb, Heating of a Plasma by Magnetic Pumping, NYO–6046 (PM–S–13) (May, 1954).

Survey of experimental Stellarator models

A summary of some of the characteristics of present and proposed devices at Princeton (some very recent—October, 1956) is given in Table 5.2. Additional remarks on each device follow.

Model A. Constructed of Pyrex glass tubing. About 350 cm in length. r.f. voltage varied up to 200 V at 250 kc. Comparison with "racetrack" shape indicated that breakdown occurred at substantially lower magnetic field values for a figure 8. Confinement poor. Now in "museum".

Model B-1. Constructed of stainless steel. Length is 450 cm. Confining magnetic field is obtained by discharge of two series banks of 0.1 farad condensers. Each bank may be charged to 4000 V. Stored energy is 10^6 joules. B rises in 30 msec and decays with time constant of about 40 msec.

Ohmic heating is by capacitor discharge through primary of transformer. Plasma is secondary of the transformer. Pulse voltage of about 100 V yields plasma currents of 1000 amp for a millisecond. Helium gas used at pressures of about 5 microns. Helium was chosen because of its convenient spectroscopic properties.

Results indicated that the plasma was nearly completely ionized and that the electrons reached a temperature of greater than 10 eV. The confinement time was of the order of 3–5 msec. The temperature achieved was appreciably smaller than expected. It is believed that influx of impurities due to energetic bombardment of the walls is responsible for the low value of the temperature.

X-rays of about 300 kV were seen. These are believed due to "runaway" electrons during the ohmic heating pulse. Since an energy of this magnitude could only be achieved by the electron revolving around the device at least 3000 times, there is indication of good magnetic confinement.

Model B-1'. Constructed of Pyrex tubing with an inner conducting coating. Angle of twist of end loops is 49 deg each. Improved coils allow operation at 25 kg. Otherwise similar to

TABLE 5.2. MODEL CHARACTERISTICS

Model	Diameter (in.)	H_{gauss}	Heating	Electron density	$T_{ev}°$	Remarks
A	2	1,000	r.f.	3×10^{12}	—	
B-1	2	15,000	r.f. + ohmic	10^{14}	>10	
B-1'	2	25,000	r.f. + ohmic	10^{14}	$\begin{cases} e > 30 \\ i > 3 \end{cases}$	
B-1"	2	50,000	r.f. + ohmic	10^{14}	$\begin{cases} e > 100 \\ i > 10 \end{cases}$	Alpert-type vacuum system
B-2	2	50,000	r.f., ohmic + Mag. pumping	10^{14}		
B-64	4	28,000	"ohmic"	10^{14}	$e > 100$	Has diverters
A-2 "Etude"	2	10,000	ohmic	10^{14}		d.c. magnetic field Variable transform
B-3	2	50,000	r.f., ohmic + Mag. pumping			Alpert-type vacuum system diverters
C	9	50,000	r.f., ohmic + Mag. pumping	5×10^{14}	20 keV	Scallops, diverters
D	36	50,000 to 100,000	r.f., ohmic + Mag. pumping	10^{15}	20 keV	Scallops, diverters

B-1 device. Experimental results are similar to those on B-1. A maximum electron temperature of 30 eV is indicated. Spectroscopic observations indicated an ion temperature of about 3 eV. X-rays of energies up to 1.4 MeV were observed. This would indicate confinement of runaway electrons for 20,000 revolutions. A kink type of instability which can develop during the heating pulse and which was predicted by M. D. Kruskal was observed. Again plasma temperatures seem to be limited by the influx of impurities from the walls of the vacuum chambers.

Model B-1″. This is a proposed machine which will have a greatly-improved vacuum system. The device will be of stainless steel, will have no O-rings and use gold gaskets. It is hoped that a pulsed confining field of 50,000 gauss can be reached.

Model B-2. Constructed of coated glass. However, one of the U-bends of the tube is of stainless steel. Has only been in operation for a few months. Length of the device is 600 cm. It has two "bulge" regions for magnetic pumping. The bulge sections are 20 in. long with a tube diameter of 5.75 in. The confining field drops to $\frac{1}{6}$ its nominal value in this region. The magnetic field is oscillated at a frequency of 240 kc in the bulges.

The initial ohmic heating performs as in B-1. Impurities limit the ion temperature to a few volts. The introduction of the magnetic pumping produces unusual effects. A very rapid heating and ionization of the plasma occurs. However, it terminates abruptly because of quenching of the oscillator. Spectroscopic observations indicate that an electron temperature greater than 100 eV is achieved. The positive ion temperature, far from the magnetic pumping section, is apparently about 20 eV. The modulation, $\Delta B/B$, is 0.7 in the bulge.

Model B-64. This device is so named because it squares all the corners of a figure 8. It is constructed of stainless steel with a 4-in. o.d. Its chief advantage is that it is of modular construction, entirely of straight sections and 90 deg elbows. Hence, modifications can be made with ease. The heating pulse is produced by a 10 kw 900 cps generator. Hence, the heating is quasi-d.c.

The diverter has been installed on this device and it appears to have a beneficial effect on the impurity problem. Both the positive ion and electron temperatures seem to rise to about 50 volts.

Model A-2 ("Etude"). This device is in the planning stage. Its particular advantages are first that the confining magnetic field will be a d.c. one, and second that the transform angle (i.e. the twist angle of the end loops) will be variable. Heating will be of the ohmic type but will have a square wave form in time.

Model B-3. Again, this is a device which is in the planning stage. It will have all the features of Model B-2 plus diverters and an Alpert type vacuum system.

Model C. Model C is the proposed intermediate scale model between B-2 and the full-scale power device known as Model D. It would have an over-all length of 150 ft and a twist angle of 29 deg. The tube diameter is 9 in. The confining field has a value of 28,300 gauss. The confinement time would be at least 0.02 sec and the plasma would reach a temperature of 20 keV. The device would have a 1% duty cycle. Costs might be in the neighborhood of $16,000,000. An interesting feature is that the magnet coils would be cooled with water refrigerated to a temperature of 4°C. This feature saves an appreciable amount of the initial cost of the power supply. It is *not* advantageous from the point of view of over-all energy production in the device.

Model D. Many of the approximate dimensions of Model D have been used in the numerical illustrations in this chapter. These will be given more accurately now. It should be remembered that Model D is the proposed full-scale power producer.

Length is 540 ft. Tube radius is 65 cm. The gas composition is a 50% D–T mixture. Calculations have been performed for three possible values of the maximum magnetic field strength 50,000 gauss, 75,000, and 100,000 (the numerical illustrations have pertained to the 50,000 case). Continuous operation only has been considered. Confinement for a minimum period ranging from 0.16 to 0.6 sec is required. The vacuum tube is surrounded by a mantle of water and lithium 2 ft thick. The water and molten lithium flow in separate steel pipes and carry the heat out of the system. Surrounding the mantle are copper coils with an inner diameter of about 8 ft and an outer diameter of about 16 ft. These coils generate the confining magnetic field.

Construction costs might be about $200,000,000 not including electrical generating equipment. If this equipment is included, the following investment costs result:

TABLE 5.3. MODEL D ESTIMATES

B	Electricity commercially available	Investment cost per kilowatt
50,000	0.48×10^6 kW	$850
75,000	4.4×10^6	280
100,000	16.2×10^6	200

Initial tritium inventories of the order of a few hundred kilograms might be required. There may be practical limits on the stockpile of tritium that can be spared for the operation of the first Stellarator. Ultimately, the Stellarator as envisioned would be a supplier of tritium since it would produce more recoverable tritium in the blanket than is required for continued operation of the device.

Some economic considerations

The numerical estimates given above for the electrical output of the various Model D designs is very revealing. These are very huge blocks of power, indeed. For example, the entire TVA system produces only 7.5×10^6 kW. Such a huge block of power produced in a single locality is generally not a desirable thing. It is hard to sell all of it locally, and the necessity of piping it to distant locations brings in large additional costs for the transmission equipment. The essential reason for the magnitude of the designed outputs is that it is very difficult to build a small Stellarator. Any attempt to reduce the size of the device leads to a situation in which more power is used in energizing the magnetic field coils than is produced by nuclear reactions. The condition that the second outstrip the first results in a minimum condition on the cross-sectional area of the tube, as will be derived below.

First, the magnet power expended per unit length of the Stellarator tube will be derived. The magnetic field in a solenoid is given by the relation

$$B = \frac{4\pi \mathcal{J}}{10}, \tag{5.54}$$

where $\mathcal{J}$ is the number of ampere turns per unit length. If the inside and outside radii of the coils are denoted by r_1 and r_2 respectively, and s is defined as a space factor equal to the fraction of the gross coil cross section occupied by solid conductor, one has

$$I = \frac{\mathcal{J}}{(r_2 - r_1)s}, \tag{5.55}$$

where I is the current density in the conductor. Hence,

$$I = \frac{10B}{4\pi s(r_2 - r_1)}. \tag{5.56}$$

The ohmic power in the coils per unit length is then

$$P_M = I^2 \rho V, \tag{5.57}$$

where ρ is the resistivity of the conductor and V the volume of the conductor per unit length. Now

$$V = \pi s(r_2{}^2 - r_1{}^2). \tag{5.58}$$

Hence, by Eqs. (5.58) and (5.56), the magnet power per unit length may be written as

$$P_M = \frac{25}{4\pi} \frac{r_2 + r_1}{r_2 - r_1} \frac{B^2 \rho}{s}. \tag{5.59}$$

On the other hand, the nuclear power generated per unit length goes as

$$P_N \cong n_{\mathrm{D}} n_{\mathrm{T}} (\overline{\sigma v})_{\mathrm{D-T}} \pi r_1{}^2 E, \tag{5.60}$$

where n_{D} is the deuteron density, n_{T} the triton density, and E

the useful energy produced by this reaction. It is convenient to write these densities in terms of the magnetic field and the parameter β. Thus, if

$$\beta = \frac{P}{B^2/8\pi} \tag{5.61}$$

one also has (for a 50–50 D–T mixture):

$$P = n_e kT + n_D kT + n_T kT$$
$$= kT \cdot 2(n_D + n_T)$$
$$= 4n_D kT = 4n_T kT.$$

Hence
$$n_D = n_T = \frac{\beta}{4kT} \cdot \frac{B^2}{8\pi}.$$

Thus Eq. (5.60) may be written as:

$$P_N \cong \frac{(\overline{\sigma v})_{DT}}{(kT)^2} \cdot \frac{\beta^2 B^4 r_1^2 E}{1024\pi}. \tag{5.62}$$

Note that the nuclear power release is proportional to the fourth power of the magnetic field strength, and that the factor $\overline{\sigma v}/T^2$ has a maximum in the neighborhood of 20 keV as may be seen below in Table 5.4. The ratio of the nuclear power to magnetic

TABLE 5.4

kT (keV)	$(\overline{\sigma v}/T^2)_{D-T}$ (cm³/sec/keV²)	$(\overline{\sigma v}/T^2)_{D-D}$ (cm³/sec/keV²)
0.05	2.8×10^{-32}	8×10^{-33}
0.1	3×10^{-28}	4×10^{-29}
1.0	7×10^{-21}	2×10^{-22}
2.0	7.5×10^{-20}	1.25×10^{-21}
5.0	5.6×10^{-19}	
10	1.1×10^{-18}	8.6×10^{-21}
20	1.1×10^{-18}	9×10^{-21}
60	2.4×10^{-19}	4.5×10^{-21}
100	8.1×10^{-20}	3.0×10^{-21}

power follows from Eqs. (5.59) and (5.62). It is

$$\frac{P_N}{P_M} = \frac{(\overline{\sigma v})_{DT}}{(kT)^2} \frac{\beta^2 B^2 s E}{(25)(256)\rho} \cdot \frac{r_1^2(r_2 - r_1)}{(r_2 + r_1)} \tag{5.63}$$

A crude estimate of a minimum tube radius can be obtained from Eq. (5.63) by inserting some reasonable values for the parameters. From Table 5.4, it may be seen that the optimum value for $(\sigma v)_{\text{D-T}}/T^2$ is

$$(\sigma v)_{\text{D-T}}/T^2 \cong 10^{-18} \text{ cm}^3/\text{sec/keV}^2.$$

In addition, the specific resistivity for copper at 20°C is about 2×10^{-6} ohm-cm. Assume further than $r_2/r_1 = 2$, $B = 30$ kG, $s = 0.5$, $\beta = 0.5$ and the energy release per reaction is 10 MeV. Then

$$\frac{P_N}{P_M} \cong \frac{10^{-18}}{(1.6 \times 10^{-12} \cdot 10^3)^2} \frac{(0.25)(9 \times 10^8)(0.5)(10^7)(1.6 \times 10^{-19}) r_1^2}{(25)(256)(2 \times 10^{-6})(3)}$$

$$= \frac{1.8 \times 10^{-22}}{9.8 \times 10^{-20}} r_1^2.$$

$$= 1.84 \times 10^{-3} r_1^2.$$

Finally, if the nuclear energy yield goes through a conventional heat cycle, a factor of at least 3 will be lost in converting this to useful work. Hence, the minimum ratio required is at least 3. Hence

$$r_1^2 \geqslant \frac{3}{1.84 \times 10^{-3}} \text{ cm}^2$$

or
$$r_1 \geqslant 40 \text{ cm.} \tag{5.64}$$

It is clear that the estimate given above is extremely crude. In an actual device, the pressure will not be uniform and there is great uncertainty regarding the possible ratio of r_2 to r_1 and the value of s. More importantly, there will be losses other than those in the magnet coils to account for. In particular, the energy required to heat up the injected fuel is not a negligible fraction of the nuclear yield. However, it does seem that radii of the order of many tens of centimeters will be required. When it is required that a tube of this dimension, with associated blanket and magnetic field coils be wrapped into a figure 8, it is clear why the various Stellarator models are as large as they are. It is also clear that a β very close to unity must be achieved if this device is not to become even more gigantic. For example, the limit on β of about 10^{-3}, which would result if scallops were not employed, is clearly disastrous.

The situation in regard to reactor control seems quite favorable. Owing to the fact that the reactor will be operating close to the peak of the curve of $(\sigma v)_{\text{D-T}}/T^2$ vs. temperature, it should be clear that the device will have an inherent negative temperature coefficient. Thus, a controlled thermonuclear reactor should be an inherently safe device. In addition, rapid control should always be possible through changes in the magnetic field strength.

CHAPTER VI

MIRROR MACHINES
AND HIGH-ENERGY INJECTION

As was pointed out in Chapter IV, the essential starting problem of the Sherwood program is the question of what to do with the ends of the magnetic field lines. The Princeton approach is to wrap the field into a figure-8 geometry. An alternative solution was proposed by Post late in 1951. His suggestion was to maintain the linear uniform field produced by a solenoidal winding, but to cap off the ends by use of the magnetic mirror principle. A major part of the Sherwood research at Livermore is devoted to an investigation of the feasibility of this method.

The features of the proposed Livermore devices will be discussed in this chapter. One of the most interesting suggestions was that the starting point of the machine be the injection of a hot plasma from an ion source, rather than starting with a cold gas and then heating this to thermonuclear temperatures. A substantial part of the Sherwood project at the Oak Ridge National Laboratory is devoted to research and development relating to high-current, high-energy ion sources. Some recent discoveries there by John Luce have suggested a new type of hot ion injection and trapping scheme. An experimental device based on this principle is being planned at Oak Ridge and is discussed in the section entitled "High-Energy Injection".

Magnetic mirrors

The magnetic mirror principle is an old and well-known phenomenon. It refers to the fact that charged particles which are moving in a magnetic field tend to be reflected from regions of higher-than-average field. It was shown in Chapter V (Eq. 5.43) that a particle moves in a magnetic field so as to keep its magnetic moment μ a constant. Thus

$$\mu = \frac{mv_\perp^2}{B} = \text{constant.} \tag{6.1}$$

The magnetic moment may be expected to be a constant under adiabatic conditions. That is, when the magnetic field varies slowly in time compared to the Larmor frequency and varies slowly in space over a distance of the order of the Larmor radius. Hence, the name of "adiabatic invariant" for the magnetic moment.

Equation (6.1) may be used to illustrate the means by which a mirror reflects a particle. Consider the situation shown in Fig. 6.1. In the region to the left, the magnetic field is uniform

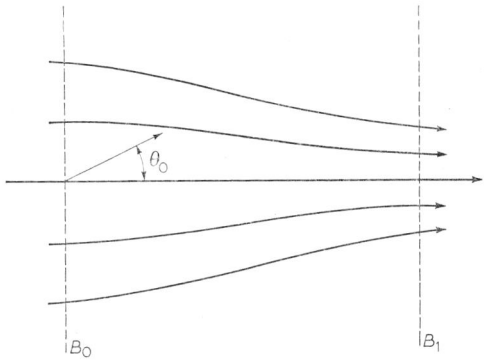

FIG. 6.1. Reflection by a magnetic mirror.

and has the magnitude B_0. The field increases on the right-hand side to a maximum value denoted by B_1. Consider a charged particle in the left-hand region whose velocity vector is at an angle θ_0 to the field axis. Thus its velocity toward the mirror region is

$$v_\parallel = v \cos \theta_0,$$

and its perpendicular velocity is

$$v_\perp = v \sin \theta_0.$$

G

Since the force upon a moving charged particle in a magnetic field is at right angles to the particle motion, no work can be done. Hence the total kinetic energy of the particle must be conserved. Thus

$$\tfrac{1}{2}mv_{\parallel}{}^2 + \tfrac{1}{2}mv_{\perp}{}^2 = \tfrac{1}{2}mv^2 = \text{constant.} \qquad (6.2)$$

Furthermore, by Eq. (6.1), the magnetic moment will be invariant. Hence

$$\frac{mv_{\perp}{}^2}{B} = \frac{mv_{\perp}{}^2{}_0}{B_0} = \frac{mv^2}{B_0}\sin^2\theta_0. \qquad (6.3)$$

Divide Eq. (6.2) by the quantity B and substitute from Eq. (6.3). The following result is obtained:

$$\frac{v_{\parallel}{}^2}{B} = \frac{v^2}{B} - \frac{v^2\sin^2\theta_0}{B_0}.$$

Hence

$$v_{\parallel}{}^2 = v^2\left(1 - \frac{B}{B_0}\sin{}^2\theta_0\right). \qquad (6.4)$$

It is clear from this result that the component of velocity along the field lines will decrease as the particle approaches the mirror region of higher field strength. In fact, the parallel velocity will go to zero, and hence the particle will be reflected, if the initial angle is large enough. Since the maximum field value in the mirror region is B_1, one can immediately write a critical equation for reflection:

$$\sin^2\theta_c = \frac{B_0}{B_1}. \qquad (6.5)$$

Any particle with an initial velocity vector which is at an angle to the field direction which is smaller than θ_c will escape through the mirror. Those with initial velocity angles which are greater than θ_c will be reflected from the mirror. Finally, if the mirror ratio R is defined as the ratio of the field in the mirror to that in the uniform region, this result becomes

$$\sin\theta_c = \sqrt{\frac{1}{R}}. \qquad (6.6)$$

A conceivable Mirror Machine will, of course, have mirrors at both ends, as shown in Fig. 6.2.

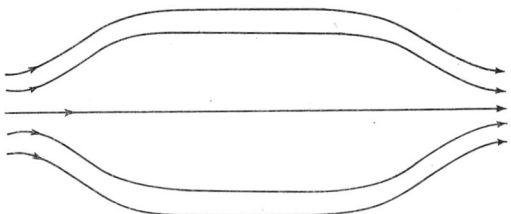

FIG. 6.2. The mirror machine.

Diffusion loss through a mirror

The most important quantity which is required for a discussion of the mirror machine is an estimate of the loss rate by diffusion through the mirrors. Upon the introduction of a hot plasma into a mirror machine, there will be the almost immediate loss of those particles whose velocity vectors lie in the two escape cones defined by the angle θ_c to the field axis. The resulting population in velocity space will be entirely depleted of velocities lying in this escape cone. The remaining particles will not remain trapped in the machine indefinitely. Owing to coulomb collisions, a particle will sometimes acquire a new velocity, after a collision, which lies in the escape cone. As a result the particle will be lost. (It is assumed here that the mean free path is very long compared to the dimensions of the machine. This will almost certainly be so.) This diffusion in velocity space represents the most serious drain of particles and energy from the system and will be calculated in the next paragraph.

Assuming no spatial dependence of the particle density, the loss rate becomes:

$$\frac{dn}{dt} \cong -\frac{n^2}{2} \cdot \overline{\sigma v} \cdot 2P \tag{6.7}$$

where $\overline{\sigma v}$ is the coulomb collision rate for 90 deg scattering by multiple collisions and P is the probability of an ion scattering into the escape zone. Just as in Chapter V, the escape probability may be crudely estimated as the ratio of the surface area subtended by the escape cone on a unit sphere to the area of the entire sphere. The only difference between the two cases is that the escape area is now a polar cap on each end of the sphere, while it was an annular region (see Fig. 5.4) in the case of the Stellarator. The probability P is now:

$$P = \frac{2\pi \int_0^{\theta_c} \sin \theta \, d\theta}{2\pi} = 1 - \cos \theta_c,$$

or by Eq. (6.6),

$$P \cong 1 - \sqrt{\left(1 - \frac{1}{R}\right)}. \tag{6.8}$$

For a large mirror ratio, this becomes

$$P \cong \frac{1}{2R}. \tag{6.9}$$

Numerical estimates of the containment time are easily obtained. Equation (6.7) may be written,

$$\frac{n}{t} \cong n^2(\overline{\sigma v})P,$$

where t is the mean containment time. Hence

$$t \cong \frac{1}{n \, \overline{\sigma v} P}. \tag{6.10}$$

Assume that $n \cong 10^{15}$ and $kT = 10$ keV. The corresponding coulomb cross section for scattering through 90 deg by small-angle collisions was shown to be 5800 barns, in Chapter II. Hence

$$t = \frac{1}{(10^{15})(5.8 \times 10^{-21})(1.2 \times 10^8)P}$$

$$= \frac{1}{700P} \qquad (10 \text{ keV}) \tag{6.11}$$

Now, by Eq. (6.8), the following values of P correspond to mirror ratios of 2 and 5, respectively.

$$P \cong 0.3 \qquad\qquad R = 2$$
$$\cong 0.1 \qquad\qquad R = 5 \qquad\qquad (6.12)$$

Hence, the corresponding containment times become:

$$t \cong 0.005 \text{ sec} \qquad R = 2$$
$$\cong 0.015 \text{ sec} \qquad R = 5 \qquad\qquad (6.13)$$

The containment time for both mirror ratios is inadequate. Furthermore, mirror ratios larger than 5 are probably unrealistic in an actual device. The principal difficulty is that a mirror is quite leaky compared to the Stellarator, for example. This may be seen by comparing the escape probabilities of Eq. (6.12) with the corresponding value for the Model D Stellarator (see Eq. 5.17). Hence, proposals for mirror containment devices have made use of particle energies in the region of 100 keV rather than 10 keV. In this region, the coulomb cross section is reduced by a factor of 100, while the particle velocities are increased by $\sqrt{10}$. Furthermore, the particle density is reduced to 10^{14} for fixed value of the magnetic pressure (see Eq. 2.20 and following discussion). Hence the new containment time estimate becomes

$$t = \frac{1}{(10^{14})(5.8 \times 10^{-23})(3.8 \times 10^{8})P}$$
$$= \frac{0.45}{P} \qquad\qquad (100 \text{ keV}) \qquad\qquad (6.14)$$

Thus,

$$t = 1.5 \text{ sec} \qquad\qquad R = 2$$
$$= 4.5 \text{ sec} \qquad\qquad R = 5 \qquad\qquad (6.15)$$

It should be noted that the nuclear reaction time for the D–T reaction is only slightly changed from its value at 10 keV. Although the D–T reaction rate is increased by a factor of 8 over its value at 10 keV (see Table 2.1), the particle density is reduced by a factor of 10. Hence, the nuclear time is only slightly changed and the mirror containment is now adequate.

The mirror containment times for a D–D reactor are the same as in the D–T case. It is clear that the containment at 10 keV is entirely inadequate for the D–D reaction (see Eq. 2.22). However, at 100 keV, the D–D reaction cross section has increased over its value at 10 keV by a factor of 35 (see Table 2.1). Hence the maximum desired containment time is now about 3 sec rather than 10 sec. Thus, from Eq. (6.15), it is conceivable that a mirror machine could operate on the D–D reaction at 100 keV.

Previous reference has been made to an improved calculation of mirror losses by Judd, MacDonald, and Rosenbluth[9]. The starting point for this calculation is the spatially independent Boltzmann equation

$$\frac{\partial f_1}{\partial t} = \int (f'_0 f'_1 - f_0 f_1) \, \mathrm{v} \, \frac{\mathrm{d}\sigma}{\mathrm{d}\Omega} \, \mathrm{d}c_0 \qquad (6.16)$$

where f is the distribution function in velocity space and where $\mathrm{d}\sigma/\mathrm{d}\Omega$ is the Rutherford differential cross section. The velocity vector is denoted by c_0 and v is the relative velocity of collision. Since the coulomb scattering is predominantly small-angle scattering, the integrand may be expanded in a Taylor series in the vector increments of velocity $\delta c_0 = c'_0 - c_0$ and $\delta c_1 = c'_1 - c_1$. Mirror losses are incorporated into the equation by assuming that particles whose velocity angles fall within the escape cone are immediately lost from the system. This leads to the boundary condition

$$f(c^2, \theta) = 0 \qquad\qquad \theta \leqslant \theta_c \qquad (6.17)$$

where θ_c is the critical angle. It is also assumed in the derivation that the distribution function is factorable, as follows,

$$f(c^2, \theta, t) = h(c^2, t) g(\cos \theta),$$

and that $g(\cos \theta)$ is nearly isotropic outside of the escape cone. The resulting expression for the particle loss rate is:

$$\frac{\mathrm{d}n}{\mathrm{d}t} \simeq -n^2 \frac{4\pi}{3} \frac{e^4}{m^2} \left(\frac{\overline{1}}{v}\right)\left(\frac{\overline{1}}{v^2}\right) \lambda_0 \ln\left(\frac{1}{\sin \theta_m}\right), \qquad (6.18)$$

where θ_m is the minimum scattering angle in the laboratory system, m is the ion mass, and

$$\lambda_0 \cong \frac{1}{\log_{10} R}. \tag{6.19}$$

Here R is the mirror ratio. The bars over the expressions in Eq. (6.18) denote the averages over the ion velocity distribution.

It is instructive to compare the result of Eq. (6.18) with the crude calculation illustrated by Eqs. (6.7) and (6.8). If Eq. (2.8) is substituted for the coulomb cross section in Eq. (6.7) this result becomes:

$$\frac{dn}{dt} = -n^2 \, 8\pi \, \frac{e^4}{m^2} \left(\overline{\frac{1}{v^3}}\right) \ln\left(\frac{b_{max}}{b_{min}}\right) \cdot P. \tag{6.20}$$

Comparing this with Eq. (6.18), one sees that the scattering probability P has been replaced by

$$P \to \tfrac{1}{6} \lambda_0 = \frac{1}{6 \ln_{10} R} \tag{6.21}$$

The arguments of the log terms have been assumed comparable and the product of the averages has been taken equal to the average of the product. By Eq. (6.12), it is seen that the loss rate is increased by the following factors:

$$\frac{P_{JUDD}}{P} = 2.0 \qquad\qquad R = 2$$
$$= 2.4 \qquad\qquad R = 5 \tag{6.22}$$

These factors are very likely over-estimates of the actual effect. For one thing, the assumption of near isotropy of the angular distribution of velocity vectors can be expected to give an overly large loss rate, since the population would be depleted near the escape cone in the actual situation.

There is an additional loss mechanism which may be of importance. This is the possibility of ambipolar effects since the electrons, owing to their higher velocity, diffuse more rapidly through the mirrors. The resulting space charge would result in an electric field which would tend to enhance the loss rate of

ions from the system. This effect, if important, can be mini-
mized by decreasing the electron temperature. It will be seen
in the next section that a lag in electron temperature may be
expected in normal operation. Calculations of ambipolar effects
are now in progress at Livermore.

Description of the proposed device

The following sequence of operations is proposed for a possible
mirror machine:
1. High-energy injection and trapping;
2. Radial compression and heating;
3. Axial compression and heating;
4. Reaction and randomizing;
5. Decompression.

These features will be discussed individually.

The original plans for the mirror machine called for a beam of
high-energy deuterons (or tritons) to be injected through the
mirrors in the first stage of operation. It is clear that a directed
beam of particles whose velocity vector is at an angle to the field
direction which is less than the critical angle will pass right through
the mirror. These particles will continue right on out of the other
mirror unless something is done in the interim which results in their
being trapped in the device. Several schemes for this trapping exist.

One possibility is a uniform increase of the entire magnetic
field during the injection process. As a consequence of the
adiabatic invariance of the magnetic moment (see Eq. 6.1), an
increase in field strength increases the energy in the perpendicular
motion and effectively increases the angle between the velocity
vector and the field axis. If the field rises rapidly enough, trapping
will result. An alternative scheme is one in which the mirror
field grows in time, but the main field remains constant. Yet
another possibility is to apply an r.f. field in resonance with the
injected particles so as to increase the energy in the perpendicular
motion. This last scheme would be severely limited by the problem
of penetration of r.f. into a plasma.

The main difficulty with these original schemes is the inability of presently-achievable ion sources to inject a sufficient quantity of plasma into the device during the time available. As a result, thinking has turned to the use of radial injection by either high-energy neutral beams or molecular ions into the device. These features will be discussed in the section on high-energy injection.

The second stage in the operation would be an increase in the magnetic field of the system throughout the length of the device. As was shown in Eq. (5.44), the square of the radius of the plasma varies inversely as the magnetic field. Hence, the plasma is radially squeezed and heated. The third step is a similar squeezing and heating but in the axial direction. This is accomplished by moving the magnetic mirrors toward each other. This mirror motion may be achieved by electrical means.

During and after the injection and compression, the plasma will become randomized through the mechanism of the coulomb collisions. At the same time nuclear reactions will occur. As the final stage of operation, the plasma is allowed to expand back out against the fields and as a result currents are generated in the field coils. This scheme constitutes a form of direct conversion of thermal energy into electrical power.

Let us consider some of the advantages and disadvantages of a mirror machine. One of the first advantages is the absence of drift effects, such as are found in the Stellarator, which tend to lead particles out of the device. Hence, it is unnecessary to devise such features as scallops and figure 8s. This has an immediate consequence that it is not necessary to build a device which must produce enormous blocks of power in order to be economically successful. This could be a very important advantage. A third feature is that hot ion injection eliminates the problems associated with the heating of an initially cold plasma. A fourth advantage is the natural way in which the sequence of operations lends itself to direct conversion of thermal energy to electrical energy.

Among the disadvantages, perhaps the most minor is the cyclic operation of the device compared to the steady-state operation at

Princeton. This usually results in poorer efficiency of operation. More serious is the problem of injecting sufficient plasma into the device. Present sources will not work for injection through the mirrors and, as will be shown in a later section, they even look marginal for radial injection. In addition, the economics are somewhat poorer. The fact that a particle energy of 100 keV is being used means that the particle density must be reduced to 10^{14}. As a result the specific energy yield in the plasma is reduced. The economic factors will be further discussed in the next section.

Before turning to this subject, it would be quite useful to point out the main reason for having an axial and radial compression of the plasma. The ions are injected with over 100 keV energy and therefore would end up near this temperature after thermalizing were it not for the presence of cold electrons. These electrons will come with the beam, or must be added, in order that enormous space charges do not develop. The cross section for energy loss to these cold electrons is enormous, as was pointed out in Chapter II. If the initial electron density is 10^{14} and the temperature is taken to be 100 volts, Post has calculated[14] that the deuterons would begin to lose energy exponentially with a half life $t = 5 \times 10^{-4}$ sec. This would represent a disastrous rate of loss from the ions were it not for the fact that the electron sink is a finite one. As energy is drained from the deuterons it goes into the electrons with a subsequent rise in electron temperature. The purpose of the axial and radial compression is to feed energy into the deuterons so as to compensate for the electron drain.

As the electron temperature rises, the energy transfer rate drops off as $T^{3/2}$. Thus at $T_e = 1$ keV, the e-folding time is now $t = 1.5 \times 10^{-2}$ sec, while the ion energy is now 99.1 keV. The e-folding time for energy input from the compression is of the order of the rise time of the magnetic field. Since this will be of the order of 10^{-2} sec or less, the compression will control the deuteron energy almost immediately.

---

[14] R. F. Post, Sixteen Lectures on Controlled Thermonuclear Reactions, UCRL–4231 (Feb., 1954).

The final electron temperature will not be equal to 100 keV. Owing to the greater bremsstrahlung of the electrons ($P \sim m^{-3/2}$, see Eq. 2.3), the final electron temperature will sit considerably below that of the ions, in the neighborhood of 20–50 keV.

Some economic considerations

Many of the economic considerations are entirely similar to those already discussed in connection with the Stellarator. An expression for the magnet power is given by Eq. (5.59). Assuming $B = 30$ kG, $s = 0.5$, and the outer radius of the copper coil as twice the inner radius, $r_2/r_1 = 2$ and

$$P_M \simeq 11 \text{ kW/cm.} \tag{6.23}$$

Similarly, the nuclear yield is given by Eq. (5.62). At $kT = 100$ keV,

$$(\sigma v)_{\text{DT}} = 8 \times 10^{-16},$$

and

$$P_N \simeq 0.04 \beta^2 R^2 \text{ kW/cm,} \tag{6.24}$$

where R is the radius of the reaction tube and an electron temperature of 50 keV has been assumed. Assume that 30% of the nuclear power is recoverable and that 50% of this amount will be used to operate the magnet. Thus it is necessary that

$$(0.3)(0.5)P_N = P_M$$

and hence

$$\beta^2 R^2 = 1800. \tag{6.25}$$

If β is equal to its maximum possible value of unity, the minimum working radius is

$$R \geqslant 43 \text{ cm.} \tag{6.26}$$

The thermal power generated per unit length is 72 kW/cm and the salable power 15% of this, which is 11 kW/cm or about 1 megawatt/meter. This is a factor of 3 less than the salable power per unit length of the Stellarator.

For reasons of increased plasma stability (see Chapter VIII), there may be a strong incentive to work with as small a value of β as possible. By Eq. (6.25) we see that the minimum value of β is determined by the maximum radius we are willing to construct. In turn, this largest value of R may be determined by considering capital costs, as follows:

The total weight of copper per centimeter is:

$$W = \pi(r_2{}^2 - r_1{}^2)\, sd$$

where d is the density of copper. Assuming as before that the space factor $s = 0.5$, that $r_2/r_1 = 2$ and that $d = 8.9$, this becomes

$$W = 42\, R^2\ \text{g/cm.}$$

If it is assumed that the cost of the copper is \$1 per pound installed, the capital investment in copper becomes:

$$C \cong 0.1\, R^2\ \text{dollars/cm.} \tag{6.27}$$

A reasonable capital investment cost is \$200 per kilowatt of salable electric power. Hence, it is desired that

$$\frac{0.1 R^2}{11} = 200$$

or
$$R \leqslant 150\ \text{cm.} \tag{6.28}$$

Upon substituting this maximum value in Eq. (6.25), it is seen that the minimum possible value of β is about 0.3. Hence, it will not be possible to operate with values of β appreciably smaller than unity.

Actually, the economic situation is somewhat worse than sketched above. It has been assumed that the only losses are in the field windings. As has already been mentioned, the thermal investment in 100 keV particles is not negligible and should be included in the accounting. Assuming that particles must be supplied at a rate equal to their loss through the mirrors, the input power may be written as

$$R_{\text{FUEL}} \cong n^2 \overline{\sigma v} \pi R^2 EP, \tag{6.29}$$

when n is the number of ions (including both tritons and deuterons), $\overline{\sigma v}$ is the coulomb scattering rate, E the input thermal energy, and P the probability of loss through a mirror after a 90-deg deflection. Now, taking the electron temperature as one half the ion temperature,

$$n = \frac{2}{3} \frac{\beta}{kT} \frac{B^2}{8\pi},$$

and hence Eq. (6.29) may be written as

$$P_{\text{FUEL}} \cong \frac{(\overline{\sigma v})EB^4 P}{450(kT)^2} \beta^2 R^2. \tag{6.30}$$

As before, choose $B = 30$ kG and $kT = 100$ keV. Now, $E = 3/2kT$ and at 100 keV, $\sigma = 58$ barns and $v = 3.8 \times 10^8$ cm/sec. Hence

$$P_{\text{FUEL}} \cong 0.038 P \beta^2 R^2 \text{ kW/cm}.$$

Now, using the most pessimistic values of the escape probability, which are given in Eq. (6.21) one finds that

$$P_{\text{FUEL}} \cong 0.021 \beta^2 R^2 \text{ kW/cm} \qquad R = 2$$
$$\cong 0.009 \beta^2 R^2 \qquad\qquad R = 5$$

Hence, the thermal fuel investment is nearly as large as the nuclear energy yield for a mirror ratio of 2 and is disturbingly close even for $R = 5$. These results were first noticed by Bing, Judd, MacDonald, and Rosenbluth[15] who have published a more careful calculation. It should be remembered that the end loss calculations of Judd et al. may be overly pessimistic. However, it seems clear that the economic balance is tighter for the mirror machine than it appears to be for the Stellarator. Since the ratio of nuclear yield to power input in fuel varies as $\sqrt{(kT)}(\overline{\sigma v})_{\text{DT}}$, improvement may be obtained by going to high temperatures. In this case, larger radii will be necessary to keep the magnet power ratio favorable.

High-energy injection

Consider the problem of injection through the mirrors. Suppose that a battery of ion sources are lined up, shoulder to

---

[15] G. BING et al., Some Calculations of End Losses in Mirror Machines, published in Conference on Controlled Thermonuclear Reactions, Princeton University, TID–7503 (Feb., 1956).

shoulder, filling the cross-sectional area of the machine just out-side of the mirror and pointed into the device. Now there have been ion sources developed at Oak Ridge which yield currents of the order of 2 amp per square inch. Assume then, that as a result of the stacking, an average over-all input current of about $\frac{1}{2}$ amp per square inch can be achieved. Assume further, for the moment, that every ion which is injected is trapped and that the injection time T is of the order of 1 msec. Then, if L is the distance between mirrors, the final ion density n becomes

$$n = \frac{IT}{L}, \tag{6.31}$$

where I is the source current. Now

$$I = \frac{1}{2} \text{ amp/in.}^2 = 0.08 \text{ amp/cm}^2$$
$$\cong 5 \times 10^{17} \text{ions/cm}^2 \text{ sec}.$$

Assuming $L = 5$ meters, one finds

$$n \cong \frac{5 \times 10^{17} \, 10^{-3}}{5 \times 10^2} = 10^{12} \text{ cm}^{-3}.$$

The final density is still a factor of 100 smaller than required for the operating state. However, magnetic compression will raise this value and improvement could also be achieved by pushing the injection time up somewhat. Although the final density is uncomfortably small, this is not the real difficulty with injection through the mirrors. The more essential difficulty is the total field rise which must be achieved if trapping is to occur. This will be calculated in the next paragraph.

Consider trapping by means of a uniform rise of field strength over the entire length of the mirror machine. Suppose that the ions are injected at an angle θ_0 which differs by only a small amount δ from the critical angle θ_c. This is illustrated in Fig. 6.3. Here the shaded regions between the dotted lines repre-sent the (assumed) localized regions of increased field strength (i.e. the two mirrors). The region between the mirrors is assumed to have a uniform field. Suppose that the field strength in the central region at the time of injection is denoted by B_0 and that this quantity has risen to the value B by the time that the ion

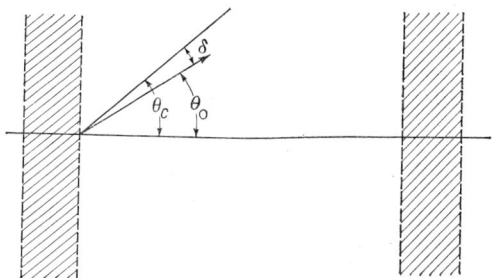

FIG. 6.3. Injection and trapping.

reaches the opposite mirror. Since

$$\sin \theta = \frac{v_\perp}{v}, \tag{6.32}$$

it is clear from Eq. (6.3) that the new angle is

$$\sin \theta = \sqrt{\left(\frac{B}{B_0}\right)} \sin \theta_0. \tag{6.33}$$

In order that trapping occur, it is necessary that this final angle be equal to or larger than the critical angle. Hence

$$\sqrt{\frac{B}{B_0}} = \frac{\sin \theta_c}{\sin \theta_0} = \frac{\sin \theta_c}{\sin(\theta_c - \delta)}$$

or

$$\sqrt{\frac{B}{B_0}} \simeq 1 + \delta \cot \theta_c + \ldots \tag{6.34}$$

Now the time interval for traversal of the device from mirror to mirror is

$$T = \frac{L}{v \cos \theta_0} \simeq \frac{L}{v \cos \theta_c}. \tag{6.35}$$

Hence the final field B is,

$$B - B_0 = \dot{B} \frac{L}{v \cos \theta_c} \tag{6.36}$$

where $\dot{B}$ is the rate of change of magnetic field. Equation (6.34) may be rewritten as

$$\frac{B}{B_0} \cong 1 + 2\delta \cot \theta_c, \tag{6.37}$$

and Eq. (6.36) as

$$\frac{B}{B_0} = 1 + \frac{\dot{B}}{B_0} \frac{L}{v \cos \theta_c} \tag{6.38}$$

Combining Eqs. (6.37) and (6.38) yields the condition

$$\frac{\dot{B}}{B_0} \cong \frac{2v \cos^2 \theta_c}{L \sin \theta_c} \delta. \tag{6.39}$$

Finally, by use of Eq. (6.6), this condition may be written as

$$\frac{\dot{B}}{B} \cong \frac{2v}{L} \frac{R-1}{\sqrt{R}} \delta. \tag{6.40}$$

The beam from an ion source has an inherent angular spread which one finds very difficult to reduce below a few degrees. Hence the quantity δ can probably be made no smaller than about 0.1 radians. Assuming a mirror ratio of 4 and a length of 5 meters, one obtains

$$\frac{\dot{B}}{B} \cong \frac{3(3.8 \times 10^8)}{5 \times 10^2} (0.1) = 2 \times 10^5.$$

Integrating, this yields

$$B(t) = B(0)\exp[(2 \times 10^5)t]. \tag{6.41}$$

Equation (6.41) indicates that after a millisecond, the field must have increased over its initial value by the enormous factor $\exp(200)$. Since the initial field value can hardly be less than about 2 kG (the Larmor radius of a 100 keV deuteron in a field of 2 kG is 30 cm) it is clear that this rise is impossible. In fact, since final fields of the order of 40 kG are about a reasonable limit it is clear that the total increase must be a factor of 20 ($= e^3$) or less. This would limit $\dot{B}/B$ to a value of 3×10^3 or less. Since this limit is a factor of 70 less than required for complete trapping, one would expect only about one-seventieth of the ions to be trapped by the maximum field rise which can be maintained.

One alternative scheme for injection is to use the method of molecular ion breakup suggested independently by J. S. Luce at ORNL, and H. York at Berkeley. This technique is illustrated in Fig. 6.4. A beam of high-energy D_2^+ ions is projected across

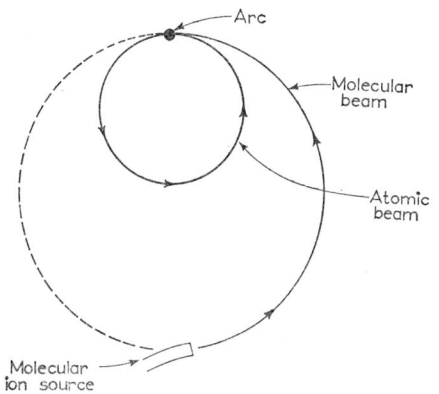

FIG. 6.4. Molecular ion breakup.

a magnetic field. The molecule is then dissociated into an atomic ion and a neutral atom near the extremity of the orbit. The resulting ion has about half the momentum of the molecule, half the Larmor radius and hence is trapped inside the field. Luce[16] has recently discovered an unusual type of high-vacuum carbon arc which can break up over 70% of the molecular ions which pass through it. The trapping scheme would then use such an arc in the direction of the magnetic field and which intersects the molecular beam at a localized point.

The advantages of molecular injection are first that injection may be accomplished radially around the mirror machine rather than through the mirror. This allows more area for the ion sources.

---

[16] J. S. LUCE, Ionization and Dissociation of Energetic Ions by a Carbon Discharge, ORNL–2219 (Nov., 1956).

H

More importantly, little or no field rise is required for trapping. Perhaps the main objection to this method is the fact that the ions are deposited only 1 Larmor diameter from the injection snout. This could lead to diffusion losses and sputtering, and hence some magnetic compression will be necessary. Plans are now under way at Oak Ridge to combine the features of molecular injection, arc breakup and magnetic mirrors into an experimental device which might enable one to grow a high-temperature plasma. The proposed device is called the DCX (Direct Current Experiment) since all features of the system are steady-state.

Two alternative radial injection schemes involve energetic neutral injection[17] and trapping of energetic particles by time-rising fields[18]. The first scheme is one in which D[+] ions would be accelerated to about 100 keV in a conventional accelerator. They are then sent through a gas target from which about half the ions emerge neutral with very little scattering or energy loss. The neutral beam would cross into the magnetic field and would be ionized and trapped by colliding with the plasma ions. In the second scheme, field rise times are still a problem although not as bad as in the case of mirror injection since particles can be injected with a very small component of velocity in the field direction. Both methods are being investigated at Livermore.

Survey of experimental program

A listing of the experimental devices at Livermore is given below. A very brief description of the apparatus and some of the reported results are included. This table is based on Sherwood Conference reports, which are particularly sketchy on these points.

Table Top I. This device is a mirror machine utilizing pulsed magnetic fields. The peak mirror field is near 30 kG with a mirror

---

[17] E. J. LAUER, Energetic Neutral Injection into Thermonuclear Machines, UCRL–4554 (Aug., 1955).

[18] W. I. LINLOR, High Energy Peripheral Injection into Mirror Machines, UCRL–4569 (Sept., 1955).

ratio R adjustable from $2:1$ to $4:1$. The field rises in 600 μsec and decays in 10 msec. The device has a 6-in. i.d. and a length of 44 in.

Injection is by means of a deuterium-loaded titanium-spark source. This "hydride" source gives a current pulse of about 10 μsec duration and delivers a plasma with energies in the range of 5 to 10 eV. These energies have been determined by time of flight and probe techniques.

The purpose of this experiment is to observe trapping and compression by time-rising fields. Containment times of 300–400 μsec have been reported. These times are comparable to the theoretical mirror containment times determined by Judd et al.[9]

Table Top II. This device has a somewhat larger peak mirror field than Table Top I and, in addition, has a d.c. field for initial trapping of the plasma. The peak mirror field is 30 kG with a mirror ratio of $2:1$. The d.c. field has a mirror value of 600 gauss and also has a mirror ratio of $2:1$. The field rises in 650 μsec and decays in 30 msec. The device has a 6-in. i.d. and a length of 50 in.

Injection is from a "hydride" source. A base pressure of 10^{-6} mm Hg has been used. Probe measurements indicate that a plasma having an electron density of 10^{12} has been contained for a time of 200–300 μsec. There is evidence that the plasma is compressed by the rising magnetic field. Soft X-rays having energies up to 20 keV appear for the duration of the containment. In addition, hard X-rays having energies up to 100 keV persist for much longer times. The hard X-rays are believed due to high-energy electrons striking the walls after the containment is over.

Toy Top. Toy Top has a peak mirror field of 250 kG with an $R = 2:1$. There is also trapping by a small d.c. field which may vary from 50 to 500 gauss with an $R = 3:1$. The field rises in 200 μsec and decays in 3 msec. The device is quite small, 2 in. i.d. and a 12-in. length. The base pressure is about 10^{-7} mm Hg.

Observations have been made for field compressions ranging

from a factor of 500 to 1300. In theory this could lead to final energies of 2.5 to 6.5 keV for the plasma, which is provided by a hydride source. There is no good evidence for this temperature. Containment times of 3 msec have been observed. Fast electrons are seen, as well as X-rays in the range from 10 to 200 keV.

Q-Cumber I. This is a d.c. machine having a central field of from 50 to 200 gauss. The mirrors have a maximum field of 3 kG and are individually variable. The diameter of the glass envelope is 6 in. The glass is coated with silver paint. The plasma source is of the usual hydride type.

Since there is no compression of an initially cold source, this device is intended only to study the behavior of a cold plasma. The very low initial fields make possible the attainment of a high β with relatively low ion energy and density. In addition, the variable mirror ratios allow a study of the efficiency of mirror trapping. Another interest is in the diffusion rate of charged particles across the magnetic field.

Results so far indicate quite clearly that mirrors are effective in the containment of a plasma. In addition, the diffusion rate is much lower than predicted by the Bohm formula (see Chapter IX).

Q-Cumber II. In order to take full advantage of lower initial fields, it is advisable to use as large a tube radius as possible. Q-Cumber II has an 18-in. i.d. which narrows to 4 in. at the ends. The central field is 25 gauss. Containment times of 1.5 to 2 msec have been observed. A $\beta = 0.1$ has been obtained. However, the neutral gas background was so large as to obscure interpretation of the containment. (The motivation in seeking a high value of β is to look for the instabilities which are expected to be present for β close to unity.)

Squash I. So named after its size which, in length at least, is as big as a squash court. The device is to have a 12-in. i.d. and a length of 18 ft and is to stand with its axis vertical. In a sense this device plays the same role for Livermore that Model C does for the Princeton group. That is, it is intermediate in size between the table-top models and a power producer. As such, work has been temporarily shelved on this device until questions of stability, as well as adequate injection sources, are resolved.

The peak mirror field is to be about 80 kG with an R of 2:1. The rise time is to be from 5 to 10 msec with a 200 msec decay rate. The total energy in the condenser bank is to be 10^7 joules. There is to be both axial and radial compression.

Saturn. This device has an equatorial ring source located on the median plane between two solenoid coils whose length is small compared to the coil radius. The source is located such that ϕ, the flux enclosed, is given by $\phi \leqslant 2\pi r^2 H$. The quantity r, in this betatron condition, is the source radius and H is the field at the source. If this condition is satisfied, the emitted particles will be accelerated by the time-rising field toward the center.

The device has two solenoid coils of 12-in. i.d. located 12 in. apart. The center field is 600 gauss with an $R = 1.5$. The source is of the usual hydride type, and the field rises in 70 μsec and decays in 900 μsec. An electron density of 10^{13} is contained for about 700 μsec. Compression of the plasma is observed and there is some indication of a final temperature of 50 eV.

CHAPTER VII

PINCH DEVICES

THE DEVICES described in the previous two chapters have at least one element in common in that they attempt to confine a plasma by use of externally-generated magnetic fields. A third method for the confinement of a plasma differs from those described above in that an internal magnetic field, produced by currents induced in the plasma, is used. Owing to the magnetic attraction of parallel currents, there will be a tendency for the discharge in the plasma to contract under the action of its self-magnetic fields. This phenomenon is called the pinch effect.

The pinch effect was first suggested in a paper by Bennett[19] in 1934. The effect was rediscovered and treated in detail by Tonks[20] in 1939. In 1951, J. Tuck at Los Alamos proposed that the pinch effect be utilized for the achievement of a controlled thermonuclear reactor. The result of this suggestion was the establishment of a Sherwood project at Los Alamos under the direction of J. Tuck which is concerned with the development of pinch devices. Pinch studies have also been underway at Berkeley since 1955. Recent discussions with the British have revealed that their thermonuclear effort is based upon exploitation of the pinch effect. Finally, the information released by the Russians to date is concerned entirely with experimental studies on the pinch effect. The Russians did imply, however, that they are investigating other schemes.

---

[19] W. H. BENNETT, Magnetically Self-Focussing Streams, *Phys. Rev.* **45**, 890 (1934).

[20] L. TONKS, Theory of Magnetic Effects in the Plasma of an Arc, *Phys. Rev.* **56**, 360 (1939).

The steady-state pinch

It is instructive to derive the relations between the pressure, magnetic field, and current in a steady-state pinch. In the absence of electric or external fields, the steady-state force equation for a plasma takes the form given in Eq. (2.15).

$$\nabla P = \mathbf{j} \times \mathbf{H}. \tag{7.1}$$

Combining this expression with the steady-state Maxwell equation,

$$\text{curl } \mathbf{H} = 4\pi\mathbf{j}, \tag{7.2}$$

one obtains the expression given in Eq. (2.17). This is

$$\nabla\left(P + \frac{H^2}{8\pi}\right) = \frac{1}{4\pi}(\mathbf{H}\cdot\nabla)\mathbf{H}. \tag{7.3}$$

This expression may now be applied to the specific geometry of an infinite linear pinch. Consider an infinite cylindrical column of plasma as shown in Fig. 7.1. The plasma is entirely

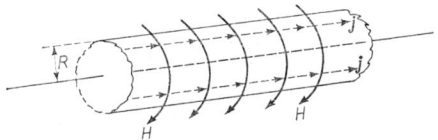

FIG. 7.1. The linear pinch.

confined within a cylindrical surface of radius R. Hence the plasma pressure is zero outside of this radius. The current flows entirely in the axial, or z, direction. The self-magnetic field $\mathbf{H}$ is entirely in the θ direction. By symmetry, all three quantities can be functions of the radial distance only. Assuming this geometry, Eq. (7.3) takes the form

$$\frac{d}{dr}\left(P + \frac{H^2}{8\pi}\right) = -\frac{H^2}{4\pi r}, \tag{7.4}$$

since

$$\frac{d}{d\theta}\,\boldsymbol{\theta} = -\mathbf{r}, \tag{7.5}$$

where $\boldsymbol{\theta}$ and $\mathbf{r}$ are unit vectors in the indicated directions. Equation (7.4) may be rewritten as

$$\frac{dP}{dr} = -\frac{1}{r^2}\frac{d}{dr}\left(\frac{r^2 H^2}{8\pi}\right), \tag{7.6}$$

which may be integrated immediately. The result is

$$\frac{H^2(r)}{8\pi} = -\frac{1}{r^2}\int_0^r r^2 \frac{dP}{dr}\cdot dr, \tag{7.7}$$

since H and dP/dr must vanish at the origin. Similarly Eq. (7.2) takes the form

$$j(r) = \frac{1}{4\pi r}\frac{d}{dr}(rH). \tag{7.8}$$

In the frame work of these equations, we are free to choose $P(r)$ as any even function of the radius which vanishes for $r > R$. The corresponding magnetic field and current are then determined by Eqs. (7.7) and (7.8). In practice, of course, the actual pressure distribution would be determined by a balance between diffusion losses and sources of fresh plasma. This complication will be ignored, and some simple distributions assumed, in order to illustrate the nature of the results.

First, consider a simple parabolic pressure variation which vanishes smoothly at the boundary,

$$P(r) = \frac{P}{R^2}(R^2 - r^2), \tag{7.9}$$

where P is the pressure at the axis of the pinch. By Eqs. (7.7) and (7.8), one finds

$$H = \sqrt{(4\pi P)}\,\frac{r}{R} \qquad\qquad r \leqslant R$$
$$= \sqrt{(4\pi P)}\,\frac{R}{r} \qquad\qquad r \geqslant R. \tag{7.10}$$

and

$$j = \frac{\sqrt{(4\pi P)}}{2\pi R} \qquad\qquad r \leqslant R$$
$$j = 0 \qquad\qquad r \geqslant 0.$$

The constant value of the current density is not a general property but instead is a peculiarity of the specific pressure distribution which was assumed.

Another possible distribution is a constant pressure P which falls discontinuously to zero at the boundary. In this case, H vanishes in the interior of the plasma and has the value

$$H = \sqrt{(8\pi P)}\frac{R}{r} \qquad\qquad r \geqslant R \qquad\qquad (7.11)$$

in the exterior region. The current is entirely a surface current in this case, and has the magnitude per unit length as follows:

$$j_{\text{surface}} = \sqrt{\frac{P}{2\pi}}. \qquad\qquad (7.12)$$

The results obtained above may be used to obtain an estimate of the pinch currents which are required to confine a plasma having the typical thermonuclear properties, i.e. a temperature of about 10 keV and a particle density of about 10^{15}. The resulting pressure is about 16 atm, or 16×10^6 dynes/cm². By Eq. (7.10), the corresponding magnetic field at the plasma surface is

$$H \simeq 14\,\text{kG},$$

and the current density in the plasma is

$$j \simeq \frac{4}{\sqrt{\pi}}\frac{10^3}{R}\,\text{emu/cm}^2. \qquad\qquad (7.13)$$

The total current through the plasma is then,

$$\mathcal{J} \simeq 4\sqrt{(\pi)}R10^4\,\text{amp.} \qquad\qquad (7.14)$$

The minimum radius of a pinch should certainly be large compared to the Larmor radius of an ion in the magnetic field near the plasma surface. A 10 keV deuteron has a radius of 1.8 cm in a 14 kG field. Hence $R > 1.8$ cm and $\mathcal{J} > 1.3 \times 10^5$ amp. It is clear that currents in the neighborhood of 10^5 amp or larger will be needed for a pinch device. Needless to say, a practical pinch would be set up in a toroidal geometry so as to avoid the end losses of a linear system.

Dynamics of the pinch

The previous discussion is highly academic in that it deals only with the static relations within a steady-state pinch under the assumption of constant current. It is even more academic when one realizes that no steady-state pinch has yet been accomplished and that all observations so far have been on the transient behavior of a pinch for times of the order of 1 msec or less. A much more interesting (and difficult) problem is the behavior of a pinch in time from the initial application of a driving electric potential. Rosenbluth has investigated this problem in detail[21] and his results are summarized in the next section.

Consider a finite conducting cylinder of radius $\bar{R}$ and length l filled with a fully-ionized plasma. If a potential difference V is applied across the tube in the axial direction, a current will begin to flow in this direction. Rosenbluth assumes that the plasma is infinitely conducting and hence that this current flows only on the outer surface of the plasma. As a result of this current, a magnetic field is formed outside the plasma in the θ-direction. The combined effect of the crossed electric and magnetic fields at the surface of the plasma results in each particle being forced to move in the inward radial direction. The situation is shown in Fig. 7.2. Here R_0 is the radius of the instantaneous plasma surface indicated by the dotted line.

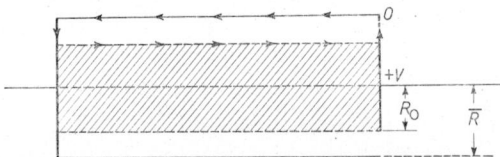

FIG. 7.2. Dynamics of the pinch.

Since the plasma is infinitely conducting, the electric field in the moving frame of the plasma must vanish. This implies the

---

[21] M. ROSENBLUTH, Infinite Conductivity Theory of the Pinch, LA–1850 (Sept., 1954).

following relation between the surface electric field in the plasma, E_s, and the radial velocity $\dot{R}_0$ of the plasma:

$$\mathbf{E}_s + \frac{\mathbf{v} \times \mathbf{H}}{c} = E_s + \frac{\dot{R}_0 H}{c} = 0.$$

Hence

$$E_s = -\frac{\dot{R}_0 H}{c} \tag{7.15}$$

Next, it should be noted that the surface electric field is not simply given by $-V/l$ due to the fact that the moving surface and changing magnetic field in the exterior of the plasma produces a magnetic induction with associated electric fields. This induced field may be obtained by taking a line integral of E around the path indicated by the arrows in Fig. 7.2. The path legs in the conducting wall give no contribution since the tangential field must vanish. The total integral is

$$\oint \mathbf{E} \cdot d\mathbf{l} = lE_s + V \tag{7.16}$$

Now, by Maxwell's equation

$$\operatorname{curl} \mathbf{E} = -\frac{1}{c} \frac{\partial \mathbf{H}}{\partial t}.$$

Hence

$$\oint \mathbf{E} \cdot d\mathbf{l} = -\frac{1}{c} \int \frac{\partial H}{\partial t} \, ds \tag{7.17}$$

where the integral on the right is over the area enclosed by the path of integration. The magnetic field in the region outside the plasma has the usual value

$$H = \frac{2I}{r} \qquad r \geqslant R_0, \tag{7.18}$$

where I is the total current through the plasma. Substituting Eqs. (7.18) and (7.16) in Eq. (7.17), one obtains

$$lE_s + V = -\frac{l}{c} \int_{R_0}^{\dot{R}} 2I \frac{dr}{r}. \tag{7.19}$$

Hence, the surface electric field at the plasma is

$$E_s = -\frac{V}{l} - \frac{2\dot{I}}{c} \ln\left(\frac{\bar{R}}{R_0}\right). \qquad (7.20)$$

Substitute for E_s by using Eq. (7.15). The result is

$$-\frac{V}{l} = -\frac{\dot{R}_0 H}{c} + \frac{2\dot{I}}{c} \ln\left(\frac{\bar{R}}{R_0}\right).$$

Finally, by use of Eq. (7.18), this may be written as

$$E_0 = \frac{\partial}{\partial t}\left[\frac{2I}{c}\ln\left(\frac{\bar{R}}{R_0}\right)\right] \qquad (7.21)$$

where $E_0 = -V/l$ is the applied electric field. Equation (7.21) is a purely inductive relation between the current, plasma radius R_0 and applied voltage. The relation must necessarily be inductive since no dissipative forces have been introduced. Equation (7.21) may be rewritten as

$$I \ln\frac{\bar{R}}{R_0} = \frac{c}{2}\int_0^t E_0 \, dt. \qquad (7.22)$$

Further progress in detailing the transient behavior of the pinch may be made only by assuming some model for the hydrodynamics of the plasma under compression. The link between the inside and outside is the requirement that the magnetic pressure balance the surface gas pressure. Thus,

$$P_s = \frac{H_0{}^2}{8\pi} = \frac{I^2}{2\pi R_0{}^2} \qquad (7.23)$$

Several hydrodynamic models have been considered by Rosenbluth. The simplest one is the snow-plow model which assumes that all material which is swept up by the magnetic piston is piled up in a very thin layer at the boundary and moves with it. In this case, the momentum equation for the surface becomes

$$\frac{d}{dt}(M\dot{R}_0) = -2\pi R_0 P_s, \qquad (7.24)$$

where M is the mass per unit length swept up by the snow-plow. Now

$$M = \pi(\bar{R}^2 - R_0{}^2)\rho_0 \tag{7.25}$$

where ρ_0 is the initial gas density. A final relation may be obtained by substituting Eqs. (7.25), (7.23), and (7.22) in Eq. (7.24). The result is

$$\frac{d}{dt}[(\bar{R}^2 - R_0{}^2)\dot{R}_0] = -\frac{c^2\left[\int_0^t E_0\, dt\right]^2}{4\pi\rho_0 R_0\,[\ln(\bar{R}/R_0)]^2} \tag{7.26}$$

This equation may be reduced to dimensionless form by the following substitutions (for the case of E_0 a constant in time):

$$\eta = \frac{R_0}{\bar{R}} \qquad \tau = \frac{t\sqrt[4]{(c^2 E_0{}^2/4\pi\rho_0)}}{\bar{R}} \tag{7.27}$$

and the resultant equation may be solved numerically.

The results show a current and radius which tend smoothly to zero in time. This is to be expected since the snow-plow model makes no provision for the effects of such things as finite conductivity and back-shocks from the center. More complex hydrodynamic models show a behavior in which an initial compression is followed by an outward bounce followed by another compression, etc. The specific results depend, of course, upon the time behavior of the applied voltage and the model assumed. A more general relation is expressed, however, by the results of Eq. (7.27). This scaling law suggests that the velocity of compression of the plasma surface is of the order of magnitude:

$$v_r = \sqrt[4]{\frac{c^2 E_0{}^2}{4\pi\rho_0}}. \tag{7.28}$$

It should be noted before leaving this subject that the Rosenbluth theory above is often referred to as the M-theory (M standing for motor), and that the same results have been obtained by the Russians. It should also be pointed out that Rosenbluth has studied the structure of the surface layer by considering individual particle orbits. He shows that the magnetic and electric fields drop to zero in a distance $\varDelta$ of the order of

$$\varDelta \cong \sqrt{\frac{mc^2}{8\pi ne^2}}. \qquad (7.29)$$

Here n is the particle density and m is the electron mass. This thickness is quite small, of the order of magnitude 1 mm thick, in cases of interest.

The kink instability

As has already been indicated, it has been found experimentally that all pinch discharges up to the present time are extremely unstable. In typical cases, the pinch may be formed for a few microseconds but then the discharge breaks up and fills the tube in a comparable time. The observation of this instability was no surprise since a theoretical prediction[22] of the effect was available quite early. A physical picture of the effect is shown in Fig. 7.3.

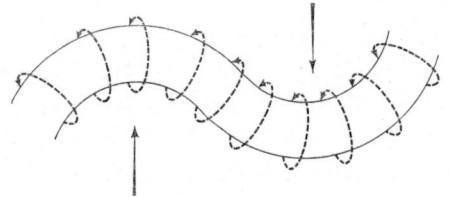

FIG. 7.3. The kink instability.

What is shown here is the effect of a lateral perturbation or "kinking" on a cylinder of plasma. The dotted lines represent the lines of force of the self-magnetic field due to the pinch current. As a result of the kinking, the lines of force are brought closer together on the inside of the bend and are farther apart on the outside of the bend. The resultant magnetic pressure is greater on the inside and a net force acts in such a direction as to increase the bend. Thus, once a slight kink develops, it will grow in size until the discharge breaks up and the plasma fills the tube.

---

[22] M. KRUSKAL and M. SCHWARZSCHILD, Some Instabilities of a Fully Ionized Plasma, *Proc. Roy. Soc.* A **233**, 348 (1954).

The amplitude of the kink increases exponentially, with an *e*-folding time approximately equal to the time required for a sound wave to travel a distance equal to the wave length of the perturbation or equal to the geometric mean of the wave length and the pinch radius, whichever is the larger. The result is an extremely fast breakup. For example, at a temperature of 10 eV the speed of sound in deuterium is about 3×10^6 cm/sec. Hence, a wave length of 1 cm will *e*-fold in less than a microsecond. A discussion of some of the observed behavior of unstable pinches will be found in the last section of this chapter.

There is a second instability of the pinch which is of interest. This is the so-called "sausage" instability. The unstable deformation in this case corresponds to a necking-down or constriction of the plasma as shown in Fig. 7.4. This instability tends to grow even more rapidly than the kink instability. Although there is no direct experimental proof of this instability, there is some indirect evidence of its existence.

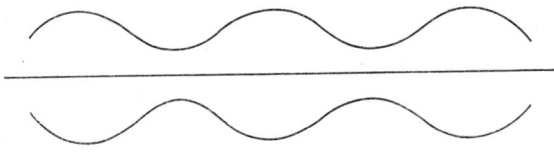

FIG. 7.4. Sausage instability.

Stabilization of the pinch

It may be possible to generate power with an unstable pinch. A discussion of this possibility will be found in the next section. However, it is clearly desirable to attempt to find ways to stabilize the system. Attempts to achieve this end have been uniformly unsuccessful until very recently when a combination of theoretical and experimental observations have led to a sharp upsurge of optimism.

It has been known for some time[23] that the long wave length

---

[23] J. L. Tuck, *Conference on Thermonuclear Reactions*, WASH–146, p. 51 (April, 1953).

kink instabilities could be eliminated by encasing the pinch within a conducting shell. Furthermore, the beneficial action of a longitudinal magnetic field (in the axial direction) upon the short wave length instabilities has been pointed out by Kruskal and Tuck[24]. However, low-power experiments at Los Alamos gave no indication of improvement resulting from longitudinal fields. Recently Rosenbluth[25] has investigated the combined action of longitudinal fields and a conducting shell in detail and has found a region of complete stability. It appears that comparatively modest longitudinal fields will suffice. However, it is important that the net compression of the plasma be small and that little or no longitudinal field remain outside of the plasma after pinching. This last feature may make achievement of the stabilized pinch quite difficult since the internal longitudinal field tends to leak out of the plasma quite rapidly at low temperatures.

Recent experiments on linear pinches at Los Alamos and Berkeley have indicated that longitudinal fields seem to suppress the short wave length instabilities, as predicted. It should be emphasized that the theoretical calculations so far are valid only for a linear pinch and have not yet been extended to a toroidal configuration.

Suppose, for the moment, that the theoretical prediction may be trusted and that there is indeed a region of complete stability of the pinch. There are still several major problems which would have to be overcome before a successful device could be operated. One of these is the tendency for the magnetic field to leak out of the plasma and into the vacuum. The rate at which this occurs may be estimated quite easily. By Maxwell's equations and Ohm's law,

$$\nabla \times \mathbf{E} = -\frac{1}{c}\frac{\partial \mathbf{H}}{\partial t} \qquad (7.31)$$

[24] M. Kruskal and J. L. Tuck, Instability of a Pinched Fluid with a Longitudinal Magnetic Field, LA–1716 (Nov., 1953).

[25] M. Rosenbluth, Stability of the Pinch, LA–2030 (April, 1956).

$$\nabla \times \mathbf{H} = \frac{4\pi \mathbf{I}}{c} \qquad (7.32)$$

$$\nabla \cdot \mathbf{H} = 0 \qquad (7.33)$$

$$\mathbf{I} = \sigma \mathbf{E}, \qquad (7.34)$$

where the displacement current has been neglected and where σ, the conductivity of the plasma, is in esu. Take the curl of Eq. (7.32) and substitute from Eqs. (7.34) and (7.31). The result is

$$\nabla \times (\nabla \times \mathbf{H}) = -\frac{4\pi\sigma}{c^2} \frac{\partial \mathbf{H}}{\partial t},$$

which may be rewritten, by use of Eq. (7.33), as,

$$\nabla^2 \mathbf{H} = \frac{4\pi\sigma}{c^2} \frac{\partial \mathbf{H}}{\partial t}. \qquad (7.35)$$

If the magnetic field falls off spatially in the conductor with a characteristic length L, its e-folding time τ, may be written as,

$$\tau = \frac{4\pi\sigma L^2}{c^2}. \qquad (7.36)$$

The conductivity of a fully-ionized plasma is readily estimated. Under the action of an electric field E, an electron has an acceleration eE/m for a time of the order of λ/v, where λ is the mean free path. Hence the average acquired velocity is

$$\bar{v} = \frac{eE\lambda}{mv}$$

and the current, in esu, is:

$$j = ne\bar{v}$$
$$= \frac{ne^2\lambda}{mv} E$$

where n is the electron density. The resultant conductivity, in esu, is

$$\sigma \cong \frac{ne^2\lambda}{mv} = \frac{e^2}{mv\sigma_c},$$

I

where σ_e is the electron–ion coulomb cross section. By Eqs. (2.9) and (2.10), this expression may be written as

$$\sigma \cong \frac{mv^3}{80\pi e^2}$$

$$= \frac{(3kT)^{3/2}}{80\pi\sqrt{(m)}e^2} \tag{7.37}$$

which has the numerical value

$$\sigma \cong 6 \times 10^{12}(kT)^{3/2} \tag{7.38}$$

with kT in eV. Hence, by Eq. (7.36)

$$\tau \cong 0.84 \times 10^{-7}(kT)^{3/2}L^2 \text{ sec.} \tag{7.39}$$

At a working temperature of 10 keV, with a pinch which is a few centimeters in radius, it seems clear that the leak time can be of the order of seconds, which should be adequate. However, the same pinch at a temperature of 1 eV would have a leak time of the order of microseconds. Hence, in order to avoid instabilities, it will be necessary to heat the plasma very rapidly so as to bring it up to a temperature at which the stabilizing longitudinal field can be held for a reasonable period.

The second major problem is the heating of the pinch. It has just been demonstrated that this process must be accomplished very quickly at first. One of the most natural ways to heat a plasma is by compression. Compression in turn is an automatic consequence of the method used to establish the pinch. As was shown in the section on dynamics of the pinch, the application of an electric field across the plasma results in a compression of the pinch with a velocity given by Eq. (7.28). If the surface acts as a magnetic piston, every particle which strikes it is reflected with an increase in *velocity* equal to twice the surface velocity. The resultant increase in *energy* is then proportional to the mass of the particle which is reflected. Hence, this method is most efficient for heating of the ions, which is a desirable property. Furthermore, it may not be too difficult to apply electric fields which result in surface compression velocities of the order of 10^8 cm/sec. This would imply that every ion struck by the magnetic piston is accelerated up to thermonuclear energies.

Unfortunately, Rosenbluth's stability studies have also shown that there is a maximum compression of the pinch which can be tolerated before instability sets in again. The criterion may be expressed in terms of the ratio of the radius of the external conductor to the radius of the pinch. This ratio may not be larger than 5 for the case of a pinch having negligible gas pressure (i.e. where the internal pressure is mainly due to the magnetic pressure of the longitudinal field). For a more reasonable case, in which the gas pressure is comparable to that of the longitudinal field, the maximum ratio is more like 2 or 3. This restriction implies that any large-scale heating by means of plasma compression must be so programmed that the radius of the pinch is not below the critical limit for times which are of the order of the instability time or longer. This is very likely a serious constraint on this type of heating.

Of course, there is always the ohmic heating resulting from the finite conductivity of the plasma. As has already been discussed in Chapter V, this type of heating is not very effective above 100 eV because of the decreased resistivity of the plasma. The most likely prospect is some kind of shock heating. One possible scheme is to create a shock by the sudden application of a large pinch field. Another possibility, suggested by S. Colgate, is to produce shock heating by the use of "collapse" techniques. In this case, the shock is again produced by a magnetic piston; but the magnetic field is an external longitudinal field produced by a solenoidal winding. The main difficulty with these shock schemes is the necessity for the magnetic pressure to rise in a time which is shorter than the sound speed across the diameter of the tube. For a tube of a few centimeters in radius, this implies rise times of the order of 10^{-8} sec. This transit time is too rapid for presently-known condensers with large energy storages.

An additional difficulty in the use of the "collapse" scheme for heating of the pinch is the necessity for programming the external longitudinal "collapse" field to zero intensity within the *e*-folding time for pinch instabilities to grow. As was pointed out earlier, Rosenbluth has shown that any appreciable external longitudinal field sharply reduces the region of stability of the pinch. Hence the "collapse" field must be reduced sharply within the time required for a sound wave to travel around the circumference of the torus (instability to long wave lengths).

One final factor should be mentioned in this discussion of pinch instability. Recent experimental observations both in Britain and in the U.S. indicate that the pinch tends to break into a corkscrew type of instability shortly after it is formed. It is believed that this behavior is in agreement with theory, since the compressions in these experiments were well beyond the Rosenbluth limit. In this case, long wave length instabilities of a helical type are predicted. The observed direction of the helix is also in agreement with theory. The formation of a helical instability may possibly have a partially stabilizing tendency inherent in it. As a result of the helical shape, the pinch current itself now tends to produce a longitudinal magnetic field in the plasma, as well as the original B_θ field. This field is in such a direction as to reinforce the original longitudinal field. Hence, a substantial increase in containment time may result from this mechanism.

Economics of the pinch

As will be shown below, the economics of the stabilized pinch are very favorable compared to those of the Stellarator or Mirror machine. The chief reason for this is the highly efficient way in which the magnetic field is produced. Not only is the plasma a much better conductor than copper, at a temperature of 10 keV, but the peak magnetic field occurs at the plasma surface, where it is needed, rather than in the coils. These factors permit larger particle densities, smaller physical dimensions and smaller input energies for the system. If the pinch cannot be stabilized, the situation is much less favorable. This possibility is considered at the end of this section.

The pinch device is necessarily a pulsed machine. This follows from the fact that the geometry is necessarily toroidal in order to eliminate end losses. In this case, the applied voltage must be obtained by inductive action, which implies pulse operation. Furthermore, as has been mentioned, stability will only persist until a fraction of the internal longitudinal field of the plasma has leaked out into the vacuum. This places a practical upper limit on the duration of a pulse. Assume now that a toroidal stabilized pinch has been established. By some sort of shock heating, the temperature has been raised very quickly at the beginning of operation to thermonuclear temperatures. The pinch is now in a steady state which will persist for a time τ limited by field diffusion.

The input energy per unit length to the system during the pulse consists of four parts. One is the energy in the pinch field. If the external field at the plasma surface is denoted by B_θ, this contribution is

$$E_\theta = \int_r^R \frac{B^2}{8\pi} 2\pi r' \, dr', \tag{7.40}$$

where r is the pinch radius and R the radius of the external conductor. Now

$$B = B_\theta \frac{r}{r'} \tag{7.41}$$

and thus

$$E_\theta = \pi r^2 \frac{B_\theta^2}{8\pi}.2 \ln \frac{R}{r}. \tag{7.42}$$

The second contribution is the energy required initially to heat the gas up to working temperature. This contribution is

$$E_G = \pi r^2 NkT \tag{7.43}$$

$$= \pi r^2 P,$$

where N is the particle density and P the final gas pressure. The third contribution is the energy in the longitudinal, or B_z, field. This is

$$E_z = \pi r^2 \frac{B_z^2}{8\pi}. \tag{7.44}$$

But, by the pressure balance condition,

$$\frac{B_z^2}{8\pi} + P = \frac{B_\theta^2}{8\pi} \tag{7.45}$$

at the plasma surface. Hence the three energy contributions above can be written as

$$E_\theta + E_G + E_z = \pi r^2 \frac{B_\theta^2}{8\pi}\left(1 + 2\ln\frac{R}{r}\right). \tag{7.46}$$

The final energy contribution is from the ohmic heating of the plasma during the duration of the pulse. If a uniform current density j is assumed in the plasma, this energy input is

$$E_R = \pi r^2 \frac{j^2}{\sigma} t \tag{7.47}$$

where σ is the plasma conductivity and t is the duration of the pulse. Now, the pulse duration is limited by the time required for the B_z field to diffuse a distance of the order of the pinch radius. By Eq. (7.36) this time is

$$t \cong \frac{4\pi\sigma r^2}{c^2}. \tag{7.48}$$

Hence, substituting in Eq. (7.47),

$$E_R = \pi r^2 \frac{4\pi j^2 r^2}{c^2}.$$

But the pinch field is related to the current density by the relation:

$$B_\theta = \frac{2I}{cr} = \frac{2\pi rj}{c} \tag{7.49}$$

Substituting this above,

$$E_R \cong \pi r^2 \frac{B_\theta^2}{\pi}. \tag{7.50}$$

Combining Eqs. (7.46) and (7.50), the net energy input per unit length to the pinch becomes:

$$E_{\text{IN}} \cong \pi r^2 \frac{B_\theta^2}{8\pi}\left(9 + 2\ln\frac{R}{r}\right). \tag{7.51}$$

It should be noted that the energy input in the form of ohmic heating is about 8 times larger than the thermal energy content of the gas.

The energy production per unit length of the pinch during the duration of the heating pulse is given by the usual relation,

$$E_{\text{OUT}} = n_D n_T (\overline{\sigma v})_{D-T} \bar{E} \pi r^2 t \qquad (7.52)$$

where $\bar{E}$ is the energy produced in a D–T reaction. Now, by the usual definition of the quantity β,

$$P = \beta \frac{B_\theta^2}{8\pi}$$

and $$P = (n_e + n_D + n_T) kT.$$

If a 50–50 D–T mixture is assumed,

$$n_D = n_T = \frac{\beta}{4} \frac{B_\theta^2}{8\pi} \frac{1}{kT}. \qquad (7.53)$$

Combining Eqs. (7.53), (7.52), (7.51), and (7.48),

$$\frac{E_{\text{OUT}}}{E_{\text{IN}}} = \frac{\beta B_\theta^2 (\overline{\sigma v})_{D-T} \bar{E} \sigma r^2}{32 c^2 (kT)^2 [9 + 2 \ln (R/r)]}. \qquad (7.54)$$

If it is assumed that this ratio must be of the order of 3 or larger in order to have excess energy to sell, one obtains a minimum condition on the pinch radius.

$$r^2 \geqslant \frac{96 c^2 (kT)^2 [9 + 2 \ln (R/r)]}{\beta^2 B_\theta^2 (\overline{\sigma v})_{D-T} \bar{E} \sigma}. \qquad (7.55)$$

Since σ is given by Eq. (7.38) it is clear that

$$r^2 \sim \frac{\sqrt{(kT)}}{(\overline{\sigma v})_{D-T}} \frac{1}{B_\theta^2}. \qquad (7.56)$$

The temperature-dependent term varies slowly with temperature and has a minimum in the neighborhood of 100 keV. It is clear that the minimum pinch radius varies inversely as the pinch field for fixed temperature.

Rosenbluth has shown that the pinch will be unstable to the "sausage" type instability if $\beta > 0.5$. Hence let us choose this limiting value as the operating condition. In addition, a compression of greater than 2.5 is also unstable for this value of β.

Hence, R/r will be assumed to be equal to 2.5. Numerical values can now be inserted in Eq. (7.55), where it will be assumed that the reaction energy is 10 MeV and the value of σ is given by Eq. (7.38). Thus

$$r^2 \geqslant 10^{-7} \cdot \frac{\sqrt{(kT)}}{(\overline{\sigma v})_{\mathrm{D-T}} B_\theta{}^2}, \tag{7.57}$$

where kT is in eV. If attention is focussed on the D–T reaction at $kT = 10$ keV, then $(\overline{\sigma v}) = 10^{-16}$ by Table 2.1 and

$$r^2 \geqslant \frac{10^{11}}{B_\theta{}^2}. \tag{7.58}$$

If comparison is to be made with the previous economic considerations for the Stellarator and Mirror device, the surface pinch field should be chosen to be 30 kG. In this case, the minimum pinch radius is 10.5 cm which is considerably smaller than the results given in Eq. (5.64) and Eq. (6.26). The two principle reasons for this advantage over the other devices are the larger conductivity of a plasma at 10 keV compared to the conductivity of copper and the more efficient geometrical usage of the magnetic field.

The situation is even more favorable than indicated by this comparison. A plasma surface field of about 30 kG implies a comparable field strength in the coil windings for the case of the Stellarator. This limiting value, in turn, is set by considerations of coil strength and fabrication difficulties. In the case of the pinch, the maximum field occurs at the pinch itself and falls off to R/r ($= 2.5$) of its value at the coils which make up the conducting wall. Hence, if the same strength limit, 30 kG, is chosen at the conducting wall, the maximum pinch surface field becomes 75 kG. Inserting this value in Eq. (7.58) yields

$$r \geqslant 5.0 \text{ cm}. \tag{7.59}$$

This radius, and corresponding field strength, will be used to illustrate the properties of a pinch device.

The total input energy per unit length is obtained by inserting the proper numerical values in Eq. (7.51). This is

$$E_{IN} = 1.3 \times 10^4 \text{ joules/cm.} \tag{7.60}$$

The duration of the pinch is found by use of Eqs. (7.48) and (7.38). This result is

$$\tau = 2.1 \text{ sec.} \tag{7.61}$$

Hence, the input power per unit length during the pulse is

$$P = \frac{1.3 \times 10^4}{2.1} = 6.25 \text{ kW/cm} \tag{7.62}$$

$$= 0.63 \text{ MW/meter.}$$

The thermal power developed is three times this value. However, the salable power should be of the order of the input power.

So far, nothing has been said about the total length of the torus. A large value of the ratio of the major axis of the torus to the minor radius is desirable in one way since problems concerned with centering of the pinch are reduced in this case. On the other hand, a large ratio of major to minor radius would require a larger total input energy and would mean a larger value of the inductance for the system. A low inductance is desirable in order that the steep initial current rise necessary for shock heating be possible. Assume that this ratio of radii is chosen to be 10. In this case, the total energy input required of the condenser bank is

$$E_{IN} \cong 10^7 \text{ joules,}$$

and the input power is

$$P \cong 5 \text{ MW,}$$

which is also the order of magnitude of the salable power.

It is interesting to note that the total input energy is inversely proportional to the magnitude of the pinch field. This may be recognized by the fact that the input energy is

$$E_{IN} \sim r^3 B_\theta{}^2$$

where a fixed ratio of major to minor radius has been assumed. By Eq. (7.56), it is clear that

$$E_{IN} \sim \frac{1}{B_\theta}. \tag{7.63}$$

On the other hand, since the pulse duration is proportional to r^2, by Eq. (7.48), the power delivered during the pulse is

$$P \sim B_\theta. \tag{7.64}$$

If the pinch cannot be stabilized, there is still a small but finite possibility of extracting useful energy from such a device. The energy production would occur only during the first compression of the pinch under an impressed voltage. After this first compression, kink instabilities would break it up very rapidly. Since only a short time exists for the reaction, very little nuclear burnup would occur unless the particle density becomes very large in the compression. This in turn implies very large driving fields.

Suppose that the plasma drives in with a constant velocity $\dot{R}$. The energy given each particle upon being swept up by the field (snow-plow model) is $\frac{1}{2}M\dot{R}^2$ which becomes $\frac{3}{2}kT$ where T is the effective temperature of the gas. Hence the input energy on compression is

$$E_{\text{IN}} = \tfrac{1}{2}M\dot{R}^2 n\pi R^2 = \tfrac{3}{2}\pi R^2 nkT$$

where n is the initial particle density. The energy output is

$$E_{\text{OUT}} \sim (Cn)^2 \frac{\pi R^2}{4C} (\overline{\sigma v})_{\text{D-T}} \tau$$

where C, the plasma compression, is the ratio of initial and final cross-sectional areas and τ is the e-folding time for instabilities. Now τ is proportional to the pinch radius divided by the speed of sound or $\tau \sim (R/\sqrt{C})/\sqrt{T}$. Hence

$$\frac{E_{\text{OUT}}}{E_{\text{IN}}} \sim C^{1/2} nR \frac{(\overline{\sigma v})}{T^{3/2}} \tag{7.65}$$

and if n, R, and T can be made large enough, it may be possible to produce more energy than is put in. Estimates by Tuck give results of the following order of magnitude:

$$I \cong 5 \times 10^8 \, \text{amp}$$
$$R \cong 5 \text{ to } 10 \text{ meter}$$
$$kT \cong 100 \, \text{keV}$$
$$E_{\text{IN}} \cong 10^9 \, \text{joules}.$$

These are very large numbers, and it seems clear that this approach is a last-ditch affair. Incidentally, one advantage of this method is the fact that a torus is unnecessary. Since the time scale is so short, the ends of the tube do not affect the interior. Hence a linear pinch may be used which makes unnecessary an inductive discharge.

Other geometries

From time to time, many geometries other than those described in this and the previous two chapters have been proposed. Most of these have perished because of some obvious flaw. However, there are at least two general classes of alternative geometries which still persist and in which some research (mainly theoretical) continues. These two general classes are the Picket Fence (or Cusp) device and devices based on ion or electro streams.

The chief, and perhaps only, advantage of these two schemes is their apparent inherent stability. Earlier discussion in this chapter has pointed up the fact that the pinch is still a very unstable system. In addition, general considerations of stability, to be described in the next chapter, had made it seem plausible that both the Stellarator and Mirror device may also be inherently unstable. It was in answer to this depressing situation that the Picket Fence was invented by Tuck. The ion stream proposal is quite ancient[19] but was revived for the same reason by Bennett and others. A brief description of these proposals follows.

Picket Fence. Intuitive arguments by Teller suggested that a situation in which plasmas were confined by magnetic fields wrapped around them were unstable. The inherent tendency seemed to be one in which the plasma slipped out between the field lines and the field lines snapped in like rubber bands. On the other hand, the same intuitive arguments suggested that a situation in which escape of plasma tended to *stretch* the magnetic lines would be stable. A geometry which has this property is the

Picket Fence[26]. A sketch of the geometry is shown in Fig. 7.5. The open circles represent windings with current out of the paper, while the dark circles carry current in the opposite direction.

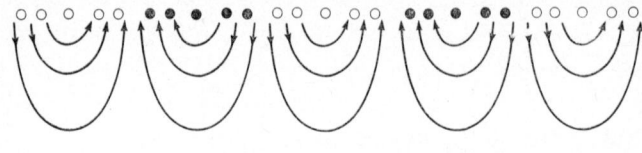

FIG. 7.5. The Picket Fence.

The resultant magnetic field is shown, along with a dotted line which is an axis of revolution for the entire figure. In practice, of course, the entire figure would be wrapped around into a torus so as to seal off the ends. Note that the plasma fills the inside volume (around the dotted line) and would tend to stretch magnetic lines if it started to leak through these lines.

The major flaw in this device is the existence of very large particle leaks at the juncture between opposing windings. These leaks look like mirrors but are even worse in that the leak zone is a line extending all the way around the tube rather than a single point, as in the Mirror device itself. A simple calculation by H. Snyder has shown that the resultant leak rate is very much larger than that of the Mirror. Hence, the device would seem to be economically unattractive.

A possible way out of this difficulty is to reduce the losses by moving the Picket Fence rapidly in the axial direction. This device is known as the "Moving Picket Fence". One way of achieving this effect is to interchange the directions of the currents in the windings at high frequency. The main drawback is the requirement for very large amounts of r.f. power which would be needed for this purpose. The same effect may possibly be achieved more economically by superimposing an r.f. field of

[26] J. L. TUCK. Picket Fence, *Conference on Thermonuclear Reactions*, WASH–184, p. 77 (January, 1955).

relatively low power on the d.c. field. The result would be a rapid vibration of the magnetic field at the points of leakage.

Cusp. The cusp device, which is being investigated by the New York University group, is basically similar to the Picket Fence. A sketch is shown in Fig. 7.6. Oppositely-directed currents in the end coils produce a magnetic field which has the proper curvature for stability. Note that mirror leaks, as well as cusp leaks, exist in this device.

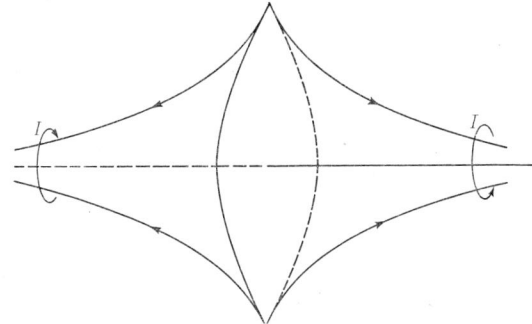

FIG. 7.6. A cusp device.

The geometry shown in Fig. 7.6 results from a rotation of a hypocycloid about an axis. Other interesting cusp geometries result from other rotations of this basic two-dimensional figure[27]. It is probable that all of these devices will remain economically unattractive because of the large particle leak rates.

Ion and electron streams. A proposal by Bennett[28] envisions the use of sustained deuterium ion streams at currents exceeding the minimum value for magnetic self-focussing. The ions are accelerated in a Thomas-type cyclotron and are built up in a circulating orbit near the outer edge of the device. Since the loss rate is presumably small, only low-density streams need be considered. Bennett states that these low-density streams of high-velocity particles are not subject to "kink" instability.

[27] H. GRAD, *Conference on Controlled Thermonuclear Reactions*, TID–7520, p. 99 (Sept., 1956).
[28] W. H. BENNETT, Proposed Thermonuclear Investigation, NRL Report 4479, RD–466 (Dec. 1, 1954).

The Russians[29] have recently proposed the use of relativistic stabilized electron beams in the design of high-energy accelerators. Although their proposals all refer to high-energy particle accelerators, it seems likely that these considerations were originally motivated by research in the field of controlled thermonuclear reactions.

Summary of experimental program

Experiments concerned with the pinch effect fall into two general categories. One is the class of toroidal pinches. The pinch currents are produced by inductive action, and the experimental emphasis is on the study of confinement and stabilization. The second type is the linear pinch. Inductive techniques are not necessary here and the pinch current may be obtained by direct discharge through the tube. Linear pinches may only be used to study the short-term (10^{-6} sec) behavior of pinches since the electrodes will seriously contaminate and perturb the plasma after a longer interval. Emphasis in the linear pinch experiments is on the study of the predictions of the Rosenbluth M-theory and the associated heating by rapid compression.

The Perhapsatron. This is the general name for a series of toroidal pinch devices which have been investigated at Los Alamos. The present device consists of a laminated transformer core linked by a toroidal tube. The Pyrex tube is 7 cm in diameter and has a major diameter of 70 cm. The overall length is about 2 meters. The power supply was originally provided by energy stored in RG–19/U cables. However, the present source is a bank of 38 capacitors each having a 1 μf capacity and charged to about 15 keV. The capacitors are individually linked by a spark gap to a single turn laid along the tube and which serves as the primary of the transformer. The torus is the secondary.

Pre-ionization of the gas in the toroidal tube is accomplished

[29] G. J. BUDKER, Relativistic Stabilized Electron Beam, CERN Symposium, Geneva, 1956.

by means of an r.f. oscillator operating at 500 watts. Initial gas pressures range from 4 to 500 microns. Upon discharge of the condensers, the current rises in about 10 μsec to a maximum value of about 40,000 amp. During this period bright pinches are seen in xenon and other heavy gases. Fainter pinches occur in hydrogen and deuterium. Smear camera observations show that several compressions occur; however, instabilities break up the discharge after a few microseconds. The observed times are in general agreement with the Kruskal–Schwarzschild theory.

Observations indicate that a maximum density compression of about 30 occurs in the pinch. Spectroscopic observations yield a resulting temperature of about 50 eV. High-energy γ-rays up to 200 keV have also been observed. Since the induced voltage is about 15 keV/turn, these must arise from runaway electrons which perform more than 10 complete circuits of the tube and then collide with the walls.

Columbus I. Columbus is the general name for the linear pinch devices at Los Alamos. Columbus I is itself a machine which has gone through a series of changes, with the particular model being distinguished by the addition of one or more super-script primes to the Roman numeral. The present device consists of a quartz cylinder with a diameter of 6.5 cm and 33 cm in length. The energy source is a capacitor bank having a 36 μf capacity and charged to 17 keV. The inductance of the system before pinching is 0.12 μh. The capacitors are discharged through a spark gap to an electrode at the top of the tube.

An important distinguishing feature of the Columbus devices is the high electric fields obtained. The average field is about 1 kV/cm as compared with an average value of 100 volts/cm in the Perhapsatron. The Rosenbluth M-theory has shown that the velocity of contraction of the pinch (which is also $\frac{1}{2}$ the velocity increment of the ions per collision with the magnetic wall), is proportional to the square root of the applied electric field. Hence, large electric fields are desirable. If a velocity corresponding to that of a deuteron at 10 keV is required ($\simeq 10^8$ cm/sec) the necessary field is easily obtained from Eq. (7.28). It is

$$E_0 = \frac{v^2 \sqrt{(4\pi \rho_0)}}{c}.$$

Assume a final density of about 10^{14}. Then if $v = 10^8$,

$$E_0 = \frac{(10^{16})[4\pi \cdot 10^{14} \cdot 3.4 \times 10^{-24}]^{1/2}}{3 \times 10^{10}} \text{ esu}$$

$$\cong 6.5 \text{ kV/cm}.$$

Hence, electric fields of the order of several kilovolts per centimeter are clearly desirable.

Upon discharge of the capacitor bank through Columbus I, peak currents of the order of 150,000 amp have been obtained. Good pinches of about 1 cm diameter are observed in deuterium and neutrons are emitted. The average number of neutrons per pulse is about 10^7. The neutrons are emitted about 1.3 μsec after breakdown and persist for 0.3 μsec. The onset of neutron emission seems to be closely correlated with the onset of instabilities in the pinch.

A great deal of careful research has gone into determining the origin of these neutrons. It is firmly established that the sources of neutrons are concentrated along the axis of the tube and the neutrons do not originate from bombardment of deuterons in the wall by accelerated deuterons in the gas. Recently, nuclear plate observations have indicated that the neutrons are emitted preferentially in the axial direction and that the center of mass of the colliding deuterons is not at rest but is moving towards the cathode. The corresponding deuteron energy, assuming the target at rest, is 34 keV. Deuteron energies up to 200 keV have been observed.

It is believed that these neutrons are not thermonuclear in origin but originate as a result of accelerations in the gas due to the large electric fields associated with instabilities. One explanation, due to Colgate[30], makes use of the electric fields produced in the neck of the pinch when the "sausage" instabilities set in.

---

[30] S. A. COLGATE, Neutron Production in the Pinch Due to Instability Breakup, UCRL-4702 (May 12, 1956).

This is illustrated in Fig. 7.7. Deuterons are accelerated across
the neck as shown. Note that the electric field must be in the

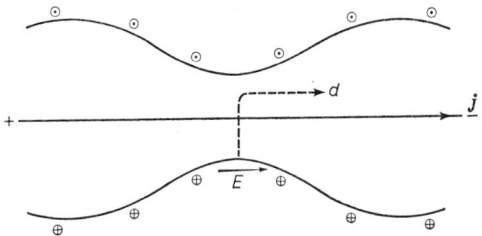

FIG. 7.7. Origin of pinch neutrons.

direction shown in order that the crossed electric and magnetic
field give the proper direction for the instability force. Hence,
the center of mass motion of the deuterons is towards the
cathode. An alternative explanation is due to Tuck[31]. In this
explanation, the electric field in the neck becomes large enough
to impart the observed energy to the deuterons by the radial
motion given in the M-theory. When the neck becomes as wide
as the sheath is thick, the deuterons that hit the opposite side of
the neck are then diverted in the direction of the cathode by the
combined action of the radial sheath electric field and the magnetic field. This trajectory is illustrated in Fig. 7.7. by the dotted
lines. The analysis of Rosenbluth, which will not be given here,
indicates this direction uniquely. Finally, the duration of the
observed neutron bursts is much longer than would be calculated
from a single "sausage" necking-off process. This difficulty is
circumvented by proposing that the instabilities occur randomly
throughout the length of the pinch during the emission period.

Columbus II. This is an enlarged and improved linear pinch
machine which is under construction at Los Alamos. The device
is designed to operate at 100 keV with an energy storage of 10^5
joules. The intended implosion times are short, 1–2 μsec, and

[31] J. L. TUCK, *Conference on Controlled Thermonuclear Reactions*,
TID–7520, p. 23 (Sept., 1956).

K

hence very fast rise times are required. This in turn implies a
low inductance system. A special low-inductance capacitor has
been designed for this purpose. This capacitor has 0.8 μf capacity at a maximum voltage of 100 kV and an internal inductance
less than 0.12 μh. The total number of these capacitors in
Columbus II will be 25. The final device will have a short-
circuit current of 2×10^6 amp with an initial rate of rise of
current of 10^{12} amp/sec.

Berkeley linear pinch. The work on linear pinches at Berkeley
has closely paralleled that at Los Alamos. Neutrons have also
been observed, and investigations are continuing on the stabilizing
effects of a longitudinal field. Particular interest at Berkeley is
centered on possible uses of collapse heating.

Magnetic induction machine. A toroidal device is being
designed at Los Alamos which will produce potential gradients
similar to those in Columbus, i.e. 1 to 2 kV per cm. An energy
source of about 10^5 joules will be used, and the voltage will be
induced in the same fashion as the Perhapsatron. A discharge
current of 10^6 amp is anticipated.

Russian pinch work. Recent revelations[32] of Russian work on
controlled thermonuclear reactions have been confined to pinch
investigations. It is apparent that the Russian results are
strikingly similar to ours. They observe neutrons and assign
the origin to instabilities just as we do. They have also developed
a theory identical to the Rosenbluth M-theory, and observe the
several radial oscillations before instability breakup. Further, it
seems that the Russians[33] are aware of the importance of a
longitudinal magnetic field for the stabilization of a plasma.

---

[32] L. V. KURCHATOV, report of Harwell talk presented in *Nucleonics* **14**,
36 (1956).

[33] L. A. ARTSIMOVICH, Lecture at Symposium on Electromagnetic
Phenomena in Cosmical Physics, Stockholm (Aug., 1956), to be published in the *Soviet Journal of Atomic Energy*.

CHAPTER VIII

STABILITY

FOR THE past two years, the central question in the Sherwood project has been the stability of the various experimental devices which are under development. It is not enough to demonstrate that a specific proposal has a sufficiently long single particle containment, and that a steady-state configuration (omitting diffusion and inherent geometrical leaks) exists in which the plasma pressure drops to zero on some fixed surface in the magnetic region. There will always be small fluctuations about this steady state, or equilibrium, solution. It is also necessary that the time behavior of the system be such that these perturbations die away in time or oscillate around the equilibrium solution. In such a case, the equilibrium is said to be stable. If the perturbations grow in time, the equilibrium is unstable.

It is generally found that if instabilities exist in a plasma the amplitude of the perturbations e-folds in a time comparable with the time it takes a sound wave to cross some dimension of the plasma. At thermonuclear temperature this is of the order of microseconds. Consequently, if instabilities exist they are much more serious than normal loss or diffusion rates. It is imperative that the instabilities be predicted, if they exist, and that methods of overcoming them be devised.

The problem of stability of fluid motions in ordinary hydrodynamics is an exceedingly complicated subject. The situation is perhaps even more difficult when attention is focussed on the behavior of an ionized gas in magnetic and electric fields. The interaction of a hydrodynamic fluid with electromagnetic fields forms the new and interesting subject of hydromagnetics. A fluid of this sort has some interesting and simplifying properties.

135

In all cases of interest the conductivity of the plasma is very large and the time during which the system is to hold together is relatively short. Hence, it is often sufficient to assume that the conductivity is infinite.

Equilibrium solutions

Before turning to the question of the stability of this hydromagnetic fluid, it is necessary to have an equilibrium state which is to be perturbed. Perhaps the simplest steady-state equations which this fluid must satisfy are the following:

$$\nabla P = \mathbf{j} \times \mathbf{B} \tag{8.1}$$

$$\nabla \times \mathbf{B} = 4\pi\mathbf{j} \tag{8.2}$$

$$\nabla \cdot \mathbf{B} = 0 \tag{8.3}$$

where P is the gas pressure, $\mathbf{j}$ the current density, and $\mathbf{B}$ the magnetic field. These equations already represent a serious compromise with reality. In the first equation, a non-linear term involving the mass velocity of the fluid has been omitted, as well as a term representing a force due to a possible charge density in an electric field. However, if attention is confined to equilibria in which there are no mass velocities or electric fields, these equations are almost correct. The most important remaining discrepancy is the use of an isotropic scalar pressure in Eq. (8.1). In actuality, this term should be the divergence of a stress tensor. In many geometries (e.g. the Mirror) the initial velocity distribution of the ions can hardly be isotropic. Even if this is so, it is necessary that there be sufficient collisions during a perturbation to keep the velocity distribution of the particles isotropic. In practice, this situation is far from true. A later section in this chapter will discuss some rough attempts at theories with a tensor pressure.

Equations (8.1) to (8.3) do not yield a unique solution, even in a given magnetic geometry. This has already been pointed up in Chapter VII, where the study of the steady-state pinch proceeded from a consideration of just these three equations. It was necessary there to choose a specific pressure distribution in order to obtain a solution. In an actual situation, one must include particle sources, diffusion losses, and finite plasma conductivity in order to obtain a unique solution. Kruskal[34] has shown that the complete set of steady-state equations may be expected to yield a unique solution. Nevertheless, it is customary to use only Eqs. (8.1) to (8.3) and assume as simple a pressure distribution as possible in order to study the stability of the resulting equilibrium.

Normal mode analysis

The earliest hydromagnetic problems treated in the Sherwood Program were, first, an analogy to the Rayleigh instability problem of hydrodynamics and, second, the stability of the pinch. These situations were analyzed by Kruskal and Schwarzschild[22] using the normal mode analysis. The starting point of this method is the time-dependent equations of motion of the plasma. These are:

$$\rho \frac{d\mathbf{v}}{dt} = \mathbf{j} \times \mathbf{B} + \epsilon \mathbf{E} - \nabla P + \rho \mathbf{g} \tag{8.4}$$

$$\nabla \cdot (\rho \mathbf{v}) = - \frac{\partial \rho}{\partial t} \tag{8.5}$$

$$\mathbf{E} + \frac{\mathbf{v}}{c} \times \mathbf{B} = \frac{1}{\sigma} (c\mathbf{j} - \epsilon \mathbf{v}) \tag{8.6}$$

$$\frac{1}{P} \frac{dP}{dt} = \frac{\gamma}{\rho} \frac{d\rho}{dt} \tag{8.7}$$

$$\nabla \times \mathbf{B} = 4\pi \mathbf{j} + \frac{1}{c} \frac{\partial \mathbf{E}}{\partial t} \tag{8.8}$$

$$\nabla \cdot \mathbf{B} = 0 \tag{8.9}$$

$$\nabla \times \mathbf{E} = - \frac{1}{c} \frac{\partial \mathbf{B}}{\partial t} \tag{8.10}$$

$$\nabla \cdot \mathbf{E} = 4\pi \epsilon. \tag{8.11}$$

[34] M. D. Kruskal, The Steady State Plasma Equations for the Stellarator Under Diffusion, NYO–7307, PMS–17 (May, 1955).

The first equation represents the force equation. Note that a scalar pressure has been assumed and that a possible gravitational term has been added. Here ρ is the plasma density, $\mathbf{g}$ the gravitational acceleration, ϵ the charge density, and $\mathbf{v}$ the mass velocity of the plasma. The electromagnetic quantities are in mixed Gaussian units and the conductivity σ is in esu. The Eulerian derivative is denoted by d/dt, and

$$\frac{d}{dt} = \frac{\partial}{\partial t} + \mathbf{v} \cdot \nabla \qquad (8.12)$$

The second equation is the mass conservation relation, while the third is the generalized Ohm's law. In most applications σ will be taken to be infinite and the right-hand side of this equation set equal to zero. It should be noted that some additional terms, which are usually small, have been omitted in Eq. (8.6). These terms may be found in Spitzer's book[35]. The fourth equation states that the motion is adiabatic. Here γ is the ratio of specific heats of the plasma. This equation implies that heat transfer within the plasma is negligible. It this is not true some more complicated relation must be used. Finally, the last four equations are the familiar Maxwell equations. Note that no distinction need be made between $\mathbf{B}$ and $\mathbf{H}$, and $\mathbf{D}$ and $\mathbf{E}$, since all currents and charge densities in the medium are treated explicitly. It is assumed in these equations that there are no particle or heat losses from the plasma and no particle or energy sources within it. Otherwise, one must include the appropriate equations.

Equations (8.4) to (8.11) represent a formidable set of relations, particularly since they are non-linear in character. Hence, the first step in treating them is to linearize the equations. This is accomplished by writing each physical variable as the sum of the unperturbed equilibrium value (denoted by a subscript zero) and a small perturbed part, thus, for example:

$$\mathbf{B} = \mathbf{B}_0 + \mathbf{B}_1 \qquad (8.13)$$

---

[35] L. SPITZER, JR., *Physics of Fully Ionized Gases*, p. 21, Interscience Publishers, Inc., New York (1956).

and then neglecting all terms of second order or higher in the perturbed variables in the resulting equations.

Further progress is made by taking a Fourier transform of the perturbed quantities in time and in as many spatial variables as possible. Thus, for example, in the case of the pinch the unperturbed solutions are functions of the radial distance r, only. Hence, one can write, for example:

$$\mathbf{B}_1 = \mathbf{B}_1(r)\exp(\omega t)\exp[i(m\theta + kz)], \qquad (8.14)$$

where m must be an integer in order that the solutions be single-valued and k may have any real value. The final step consists in solving the set of coupled, homogeneous ordinary differential equations resulting from the substitution of Eq. (8.14) in the linearized relations subject to the proper boundary conditions. The final result is in the form of a single "characteristic" equation which is a function of ω, k, m, and the unperturbed variables. The system is unstable or stable depending on whether or not there exist solutions of this "characteristic" equation with ω having a real positive part.

The results of Kruskal and Schwarzschild[22] for the case of the ordinary pinch have already been described in Chapter VII. The $m = 1$ mode, which corresponds to the "kink" perturbation, was found to be unstable for all wavelengths k. The $m = 0$ mode, which is the "sausage" instability, is also unstable for all wavelengths[24] while the higher modes $m \geqslant 2$ are unstable only for sufficiently small wavelengths.

The first problem treated in ref. 22 was the case of an infinitely conducting fluid supported against gravity by a magnetic field. This equilibrium, in complete analogy to the Rayleigh instability problem, was also found to be unstable.

Kruskal and Tuck[24] then added a magnetic field to the pinch in the longitudinal direction both inside the plasma and out. It was found that this stabilized the short wave length instabilities. Finally, the recent work of Rosenbluth[25] (using a form of the variational technique to be described in the next section) considered the combined effect of an internal longitudinal field and an external conducting shell. The results indicated that there were indeed regions of complete stability of the pinch but with some strong restrictions on the maximum compression of the pinch and on the maximum value of the external longitudinal field.

A diagram of some of the results given by Rosenbluth is shown in Fig. 8.1. This result is for the case of no longitudinal field

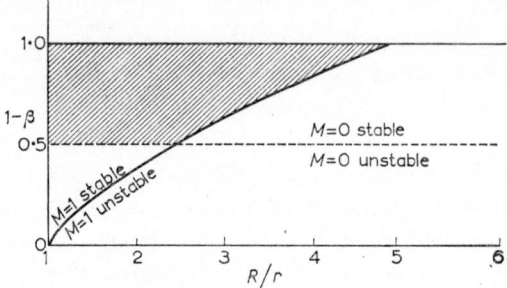

FIG. 8.1. Stability zone for no external B_z.

external to the pinch. The quantity β is the ratio of the constant material pressure in the pinch to the external magnetic pressure at the boundary. Hence,

$$\beta = \frac{8\pi P}{B_\theta^2(r)} = 1 - \frac{B_z^2}{B_\theta^2(r)}. \qquad (8.15)$$

The external conductor radius is denoted by R and the pinch radius by r. It was found that the $m = 0$ mode was unstable for any compression if $\beta > 0.5$. In addition, the $m = 1$ mode is unstable at a given value of β for any compression greater than a number varying between 1 and 5. No stability at all exists for $R/r > 5$. The region of complete stability is indicated by the shaded zone in Fig. 8.1. A similar diagram may be drawn for any other given value of the external B_z field. The general nature of these results is that the zone of stability shrinks to the left of the diagram as the external B_z field increases in value. For example, when B_z^2 external is equal to $\frac{1}{2}B_\theta^2(r)$, there is no stability at all for R/r greater than about 1.85 and the maximum compression for β of 0.5 is about 1.2.

It is of interest to note that the stabilizing tendency of the B_z field is entirely dependent upon its being embedded in the plasma. A recent calculation of R. J. Mackin and A. Simon (unpublished) considered the case of a linear coaxial cylinder of plasma with longitudinal fields existent in the hollow center of the cylinder, in the plasma itself and external to the cylinder. It was found that the trapped magnetic field in the hollow center of the pinch did not contribute to stability (in fact, it had no effect at all on the $m = 0$ instabilities) and that this function is entirely performed by the longitudinal field in the plasma itself.

The variational method

The method of normal mode analysis was historically the first to be applied to Sherwood stability problems. In particular, it was and is a good method for analyzing simple geometries, such as the pinch, in which one can solve the resulting differential equations to obtain the normal modes. The method is considerably less flexible when more complicated geometries are considered.

Interest in the more complicated geometries was aroused by Edward Teller at the 1954 Princeton meeting when he expressed doubts that any of the systems we were dealing with were stable. He likened containment of the plasma by magnetic fields to containment of a gas by a large number of rubber bands, which would be highly unstable, and illustrated his remarks by the following example. Let the magnetic field be excluded from the

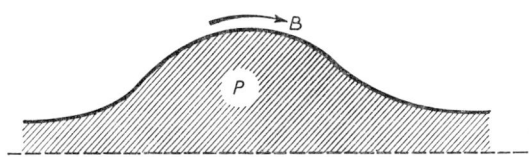

FIG. 8.2. Magnetically confined bulge.

plasma and let the system be cylindrically symmetric with a bulge, as shown in Fig. 8.2. The dotted line is the axis of symmetry of the system and the trace of the surface in the plane of the paper is a line of magnetic flux. Assume that a small ripple occurs on the surface, and that this ripple occurs all along its included flux lines. Thus a cross section of the plasma at any axial point has the form shown in Fig. 8.3.

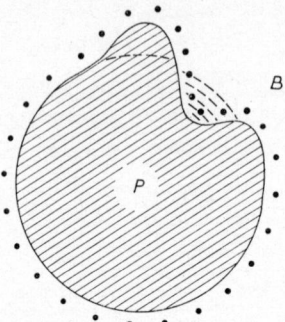

FIG. 8.3. Surface ripple.

Assume that the ripple preserves the volume of the plasma. In that case the plasma pressure and hence the plasma energy is unchanged. Assume further that the flux lines which were in the shaded region above the dotted line are now moved into the newly-available volume in the trough of the ripple and under the dotted line, and that the remainder of the magnetic field is undisturbed. Owing to the curvature of the bulge, the area in the shaded region above the dotted line must be somewhat smaller than the area in the trough below the dotted line if the total volumes are to be equal. Hence, the magnetic field strength is reduced somewhat in the trough and the total magnetic field energy is reduced. The total potential energy of the system has decreased as a result of this ripple and so the system is unstable to this perturbation.

It was shown almost immediately that Teller's particular argument was wrong, but that his intuitive idea was correct. The only error in his argument is the extension of the ripple all along the included lines of magnetic flux. The regions of reverse curvature at the left and right of the bulge in Fig. 8.2 have

a reverse effect on the potential energy change and actually overcome the instability produced by the central section of positive
curvature. The system *is* unstable to little "flutes" or ripples
which do not extend the whole length along a line of force but
terminate before the curvature changes sign.

Perhaps another way to see the instability of the plasma is by
an argument due to Conrad Longmire. If the flutes are *very
thin* they leave the rest of the magnetic field undisturbed moving
only a little flux and keeping the plasma pressure constant.
Since the field decreases outward because of its curvature the
same gas pressure meets a lower magnetic pressure at the top of
the very thin flute and the flute continues to grow.

Since the instability problem was serious for almost all geometries of interest a general theory seemed desirable. A very
powerful technique is available by use of variational methods
and this is known as the δW formalism. Consider a displacement
perturbation $\xi(\mathbf{r})$ of the material of the plasma. Imagine pincers
from outside displacing every element of plasma through a distance $\xi(\mathbf{r})$. Since the matter is nearly infinitely conducting the
lines of force are frozen in the plasma. From their varying
density one can calculate the new field strength at the end of
the displacement. In addition, knowing the varying density of
the plasma and assuming adiabatic compression allows one to
calculate the change in gas pressure. These two results allow a
calculation of the change in total potential energy of the system.

Let the total potential energy by denoted by W. Then,

$$W = \int \left(\frac{B^2}{8\pi} + \frac{P}{\gamma - 1}\right) d\tau, \qquad (8.16)$$

where the integration is over all space. It can be shown that
the change in W due to a displacement $\xi(\mathbf{r})$ is

$$\delta W = \frac{1}{8\pi} \int \{[\nabla \times (\xi \times \mathbf{B})]^2 + \mathbf{j} \cdot \xi \times [\nabla \times (\xi \times \mathbf{B})]$$

$$+ 4\pi\gamma P(\nabla \cdot \xi)^2 + 4\pi(\xi \cdot \nabla P)(\nabla \cdot \xi)\} d\tau, \qquad (8.17)$$

where B and P are equilibrium values. If δW is positive external work must be done to carry out the displacement and the system is stable to this $\xi(\mathbf{r})$. If δW is negative the system is unstable.

It may be shown that the ratio

$$\lambda^2 = -\frac{\delta W}{\frac{1}{2}\int \rho\xi^2\,d\tau}, \tag{8.18}$$

where ρ is the equilibrium density, is stationary (i.e. maximum, minimum, or saddle point) with regard to the possible displacement functions $\xi(\mathbf{r})$ whenever $\xi(\mathbf{r})$ corresponds to an eigenmode of the system. In such cases, the time behavior of the displacement is

$$\xi(\mathbf{r},t) = \xi(\mathbf{r})\,e^{\omega t} \tag{8.19}$$

and $\lambda^2 = \omega^2.$

Hence, if a displacement is found which makes δW negative, one is assured that there exists at least one unstable eigenmode of the system with an eigenvalue ω^2 which is

$$\omega^2 \geqslant \lambda^2, \tag{8.20}$$

where λ^2 is the ratio given by Eq. (8.18) for this displacement. Hence, a minimum value can be found for the blowup rate. The precise value can only be found by actually determining the stationary displacements for the system. It is important to note that the *existence* of an instability can be detected simply by finding any $\xi(\mathbf{r})$ which makes δW negative and that it is not necessary to obtain the stationary values unless information on ω^2 and the shape of the eigenmodes is required. The reader should note than when fluid–vacuum and fluid–fluid boundaries exist, there are some restrictions on the possible forms of the displacement.

Using this variational method[36] the following results were found. Consider any cylindrically symmetric equilibrium system in which B_θ is zero so that the lines of force lie in planes which

---

[36] E. FRIEMAN et al., Stability Criteria, *Conference on Controlled Thermonuclear Reactions*, TID–7503 (Feb., 1956).

include the axis. One of these planes in shown in Fig. 8.4 and illustrates the case of a bulge in the field lines. To each line of

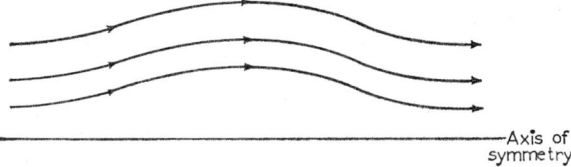

FIG. 8.4. Magnetic surfaces.

flux in this diagram there corresponds a magnetic surface which is generated by rotating the line of flux about the axis. Denote the flux contained between this surface and the axis by ψ. The quantity ψ is a natural coordinate of the problem. Let P be the value of the pressure on the magnetic surface, V the volume contained inside this surface and let P' and V' be the derivatives of these quantities *with respect to* ψ. Then, for systems in which the gas pressure is low (small β) and also for a number of large β cases the system is stable or unstable as $M''V''/M'V'$ is positive or negative,

$$\frac{M''V''}{M'V'} \gtreqless 0 \begin{cases} \text{stability} \\ \text{neutral} \\ \text{unstable} \end{cases} \tag{8.21}$$

where

$$\frac{M''}{M'} = \frac{V''}{V'} + \frac{P'}{\gamma P} \tag{8.22}$$

It may be shown that a system in which the magnetic lines are concave toward the axis (which is the case illustrated in Fig. 8.4) has a positive value of V''/V'. Hence, stability is possible only if M''/M' is positive.

By Eq. (8.22) this implies that if the gas pressure decreases outwards it must not be so rapid that P'/P is more negative than V''/V' is positive. However, if a plasma is confined, its pressure P must drop to zero at some finite distance. This will make M''/M' negative unless V''/V' goes to infinity at the same point. This can only happen if B becomes infinite.

If the gas pressure increases outwards, one can only make this compatible with containment by having a sudden discontinuity in pressure at some surface. A similar analysis, then, shows that the surface will be extremely unstable to such things as "flute" instabilities.

Thus it may be expected that the "bulge" regions of the Stellarator as well as the central regions of the Mirror Machine will be unstable and some stabilizing mechanism must be sought. It also seems clear that the devices with reverse curvature of the magnetic lines, such as the Picket Fence and Cusp devices, should be inherently stable.

Stabilization of the Stellarator

Spitzer has suggested that an external magnetic field transverse to the main B_z field of the Stellarator would tend to bind the lines of force and thus stabilize the system. This suggestion has resulted in the investigation[37] by variational techniques of a number of problems involving transverse fields superimposed on the main B_z field. In most of these problems, transverse fields with helical symmetry have been used. It has been found that the stabilizing effect of the transverse field is due to a nonuniform twist of the field lines. Thus if F' represents the twist or rotational transform angle of the flux on a magnetic surface, the beneficial effect is due to the existence of a non-zero F''. The result of these calculations leads to the speculation that the general form for δW in such systems is

$$\delta W \sim M''(V'' - P'L') + (F'')^2$$

where L' is the weighted average of B^{-2} over a flux tube. Thus one can achieve greater stability with systems whose F'' is large.

This stabilizing action may be viewed in another way. At the interface the external lines of force make an angle with the internal lines of force. If a flute tried to follow the external lines of force it would wrinkle the internal lines. In the same way a

---

[37] E. FRIEMAN, Recent Results on Stability, *Conference on Controlled Thermonuclear Reactions*, TID–7520 (Sept., 1956).

flute following the internal lines would wrinkle the external ones. If the change in angle (F'') is large enough the situation becomes stable to flute instabilities.

Research is continuing on methods of stabilizing the Stellarator. It appears that modest transverse fields will stabilize systems with small β, but not those with $\beta = 1$. Some consideration is being given to eliminating the figure 8 entirely and using a helically-wound torus in its place.

Similar considerations may also apply to the Mirror Machine. In addition, attention is being paid to possible beneficial effects resulting from terminating the magnetic lines beyond the mirror on a metal plate (thus tying down the lines) and to the possible effect of conduction along the field lines smearing out the electric fields which accompany instabilities.

Some miscellaneous results

There has been a great deal of research on the problem of stability in the Sherwood Project. It would not be possible to describe all the work in detail in a set of survey lectures such as these. Instead, a few selected topics will be briefly described in the remainder of this chapter.

Heating instability in the Stellarator. The confining field of the Stellarator is a longitudinal B_z field which undergoes a rotational transform in a single revolution around the device. If a heating current is passed through the Stellarator, this current produces a B_θ field which tends to alter the twist, or rotational transform, of the Stellarator field. Kruskal[38] has shown that there is a limiting value of this current above which instability sets in.

Actually, there are two limits depending on which direction the current is going. One may attribute the instability to the removal of the rotational transform by the θ-field of the current. In one direction the rotational twist is removed. In the other

---

[38] M. KRUSKAL, Large Scale Plasma Instability in the Stellarator, PM–S–12, NYO–6045 (April, 1954).

direction it is pushed up to 360 deg. The critical limits are proportional to B_z/L where L is the Stellarator length. These differing critical currents have actually been observed.

Rayleigh's Principle and rotation. The success of the variational method described earlier depends upon the existence of a Rayleigh Principle for the equilibrium system. One way of stating this is that the Hamiltonian of the system shall be separable into a kinetic energy term and a potential energy term with no cross term. Another way of stating this is to require that there be no velocity-dependent forces in the perturbed equations. If a Rayleigh Principle exists for the system, one is assured that the square of the eigenvalues, ω^2, is real and hence that each eigenmode is purely oscillatory or purely exponential in its time behavior. If a Rayleigh Principle does not exist, the eigenvalues are complex and the simple variational methods of Eqs. (8.17) to (8.20) are not useful.

Kruskal has shown that a Rayleigh Principle exists for a hydromagnetic fluid which has no electric fields or mass velocity in its equilibrium state. This requirement has been true for all cases considered by the Princeton group. There is, however, at least one case of interest in which mass velocity does exist in the steady state. Snyder[39] has suggested that the kink instability of the pinch might be overcome by imparting a mechanical rotation to the pinched fluid about its axis of symmetry. This suggestion is being investigated at Oak Ridge.

Owing to the fact that variational techniques cannot be used, the problem has been attacked by a numerical scheme. The method is to make use of a high-speed digital computer (the ORACLE) to integrate the perturbed equations in time. The initial equilibrium is perturbed and the subsequent behavior is watched. If unstable modes exist they should become dominant in time. The results[40] which have been obtained so far are somewhat

---

[39] H. SNYDER, Effect of Rotational Motion on Plasma Stability, *Conference on Thermonuclear Reactions*, WASH–289, p. 351 (June, 1955).

[40] F. M. RANKIN and A. SIMON, ORACLE Calculations of Stability, *Conference on controlled Thermonuclear Reactions*, TID–7503 (Feb., 1956).

obscured because of the effects of inherent numerical instabilities produced by the use of a finite difference scheme and by round-off errors. However, there is indication that rotation does not produce stability. It does appear to have a stabilizing influence on the low k (or long wave length) modes.

Tensor pressure. Perhaps the most serious assumption in the variational method is the assumption that the equilibrium pressure is a scalar and that there are enough collisions during an instability to keep the velocity distribution of the particles isotropic. Rosenbluth has considered one aspect of this problem in his paper on stability of the pinch[25]. He assumes a non-isotropic distribution of particle velocities in the equilibrium state. He then uses the adiabatic invariants of the motion to calculate the effect of a perturbation on the orbit of a single particle, and sums over all orbits to obtain the result. The result reduces to that obtained in the magnetohydrodynamic approximation when the velocity distribution is isotropic. In the more general case, the results depend on $(P_1 - P_3)$ where P_1 is the pressure in the direction of the field lines and P_3 the pressure at right angles to the field lines. If $P_3 > P_1$, the pinch is less stable than in the isotropic case. More general considerations along these lines have been given by Brueckner, Chew, Goldberger, Longmire, Low, and Watson[41].

---

[41] Series of Lectures on Physics of Ionized Gases, LA–2055 (Oct., 1956).

CHAPTER IX

DIFFUSION
ACROSS A MAGNETIC FIELD

AT ONE time in the development of the Sherwood Project, the magnitude of the effective diffusion coefficient in a fully-ionized gas was of vital concern. This question is far from settled, particularly since it has not yet been possible to measure this coefficient in a fully-ionized plasma. However, uncertainty on this score has been far overshadowed by questions of plasma instabilities. In part, this is due to the more disastrous effect of such instabilities if they occur. A second reason is that investigations at Oak Ridge have shown that the observed diffusion coefficient in a *weakly-ionized plasma* is in agreement with the classical collision-diffusion picture and that some early observations at Berkeley, which indicated an anomalously high rate, were improperly interpreted.

The first part of this chapter will discuss the theory and experiments relating to diffusion in a weakly-ionized plasma. The last part of the chapter will discuss the predictions of the classical collision-diffusion theory for diffusion in a fully-ionized plasma.

WEAKLY-IONIZED PLASMA

Diffusion coefficient

The diffusion coefficient may be estimated by the use of some crude kinetic theory considerations. The result is not as accurate as that obtained by use of the Boltzmann equation but, as is usual, it will differ from that exact result by a factor of 2 or less. First, consider a problem with no magnetic field present. A gas of particles, whose diffusion rate we wish to calculate, is continually colliding with a matrix of fixed collision centers. It is assumed that the particles are monoenergetic, that their distribution of velocities after collision is isotropic, and that the particle density, $n(x)$, varies only in the x-direction. The situation is sketched in Fig. 9.1. The flux of particles passing through a

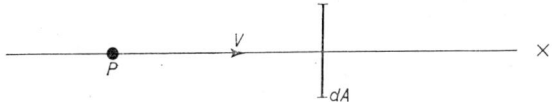

FIG. 9.1. Ordinary diffusion.

small area, dA, normal to the x-direction and at $x = 0$ is obtained by integrating over all particles which collide somewhere and then pass through dA. For example, the collision rate per unit volume at point P is

$$\text{C.R.} = n(P)\frac{v}{\lambda}, \tag{9.1}$$

where v is the particle velocity and λ is the mean free path for collision with the target centers. Of those colliding, only $\frac{1}{3}$ then move in the direction of the x-axis (this allows for the other two dimensions) and only $\frac{1}{2}$ of these move toward dA rather than away. Finally, the probability of these particles reaching dA without another collision is expressed by the usual exponential $\exp\{-|x|/\lambda\}$. Hence the flux per unit area due to collisions in a unit volume at point P is

$$= \frac{nv}{6\lambda}\exp[-(|x|/\lambda)] \tag{9.2}$$

and the total flux is obtained by integrating over all space. Thus:

$$F = \frac{v}{6\lambda}\left\{ \int_{-\infty}^{} n(x)\exp(x/\lambda)dx - \int_{0}^{\infty} n(x)\exp(-x/\lambda)dx \right\}. \tag{9.3}$$

Expand $n(x)$ in a Taylor series about the origin. The leading terms cancel, while the next term yields the following result:

$$F = -\frac{v}{3\lambda}\frac{dn}{dx} \cdot \int_0^\infty x \exp(-x/\lambda)\ dx$$

$$= -\frac{\lambda v}{3} \cdot \frac{dn}{dx}. \tag{9.4}$$

The diffusion coefficient is, by definition, the coefficient of the density gradient. Hence

$$D_0 = \frac{\lambda v}{3}. \tag{9.5}$$

The situation in the presence of a magnetic field is considerably more complicated. The particles no longer travel in a straight line between collisions but rather move on a circular path. Nevertheless, a simple answer may be obtained by using a "curved one-dimensional" geometry. Figure 9.2 illustrates the

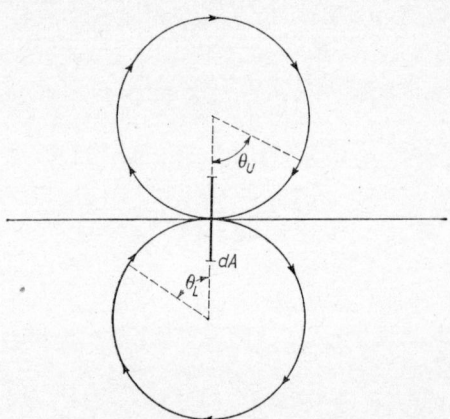

FIG. 9.2. Diffusion in a magnetic field.

geometry. Particles passing in the normal direction through the area dA from the left arise from collisions which have occurred somewhere on the lower circle of Larmor radius r_0. Similarly, those passing through dA from the right have originated from collisions at some earlier time on the upper circle. If the distance from dA back along either path is denoted by s, the particle flux from the left by the same argument as before is:

$$F_+ = \int_0^\infty n(s_L) \frac{v}{6\lambda} \exp(-s_L/\lambda) \, ds_L,$$

and that from the right is

$$F_- = \int_0^\infty n(s_U) \frac{v}{6\lambda} \exp(-s_U/\lambda) \, ds_U,$$

where s_L and s_U measure the path lengths back along the lower and upper loop respectively.

Assume as before that n varies only in the x-direction and that a Taylor series expansion is performed in the x-direction. The leading term vanishes as before. The next term yields:

$$F = \frac{v}{6\lambda} \frac{dn}{dx}\left\{ \int_0^\infty x_L \exp(-s_L/\lambda) \, ds_L - \int_0^\infty x_U \exp(-s_U/\lambda) \, ds_U \right\}$$

Now, in terms of the angles in Fig. 9.2,

$$s_L = r_0 \theta_L$$
$$s_U = r_0 \theta_U$$
$$x_L = -r_0 \sin \theta_L$$
$$x_U = r_0 \sin \theta_U.$$

Hence

$$F = -\frac{v r_0^2}{3\lambda} \frac{dn}{dx} \int_0^\infty \sin \theta \exp[-(r_0/\lambda)\theta] d\theta. \tag{9.6}$$

The integral can be performed (see Pierce 414) and the result is

$$F = -\frac{v r_0^2}{3\lambda} \frac{1}{1 + (r_0/\lambda)^2} \frac{dn}{dx}$$
$$= -\frac{\lambda v}{3} \frac{1}{1 + (\lambda/r_0)^2} \frac{dn}{dx}.$$

The new diffusion coefficient is now

$$D = \frac{\lambda v}{3} \frac{1}{1 + (\lambda/r_0)^2} \tag{9.7}$$

Note that this reduces properly to the field-free value given in Eq. (9.5) when B vanishes, since the Larmor radius r_0 becomes infinite in that limit. The denominator may also be written in an alternative form by noting that the Larmor radius is connected to the angular frequency by the relation

$$r_0 \omega = v \tag{9.8}$$

and that the mean free time between collisions, τ, is

$$\tau = \frac{\lambda}{v}. \tag{9.9}$$

Thus,

$$D_\perp = \frac{D_0}{1 + (\omega \tau)^2} \tag{9.10}$$

where the subscript 0 denotes the field-free diffusion coefficient of Eq. (9.5) and the subscript $\perp$ indicates the corresponding coefficient across a magnetic field.

The diffusion coefficient in the direction of the magnetic field will be the same as in the absence of a magnetic field since a particle moving in this direction will experience no magnetic force. Denoting the diffusion coefficient in the field direction as $D_\parallel$, one has

$$D_\parallel = D_0 = \frac{\lambda v}{3}. \tag{9.11}$$

Ambipolar diffusion

A realistic plasma has two types of charged particles, electrons and ions, and will have almost precise charge neutrality except in a thin sheath region close to a material wall. The requirement of near-neutrality is easily shown. Suppose that the electron density in a plasma is denoted by n and that the ions are entirely absent over a thin slab-like region of the plasma of half-thickness x. The resultant potential difference from the center to the outside of the slab region is readily calculated

$$\frac{\partial^2 V}{\partial x^2} = 4\pi n e$$

and
$$\Delta V = 2\pi n e \cdot x^2.$$

The change in potential energy of an electron across this slab is then

$$\Delta E = 2\pi n e^2 x^2.$$

It is convenient to define a characteristic length in a plasma, denoted by h, which is the value of x for which the change in potential energy equals the mean kinetic energy, $\frac{1}{2}kT$, in one direction. Thus

$$h = \sqrt{\frac{kT}{4\pi n e^2}}. \qquad (9.12)$$

This quantity h is called the "Debye shielding length" since it is clearly a measure of the distance over which the electron charge density can differ appreciably from the ion charge density. For example, over a region whose thickness is ten times h, the electron charge density must equal the ion charge density within 1% if the electrical potential energy is not to exceed the mean kinetic energy. Of course, the electrical potential energy cannot be larger than the mean thermal energy since the charged particles will then move so as to restore neutrality.

It is assumed that h is small compared to other lengths of interest in the plasma. In fact, this is the definition of a plasma. If kT is in electron volts, Eq. (9.12) may be rewritten as

$$h = 740 \sqrt{\frac{kT}{n}} \text{ cm.} \qquad (9.13)$$

A typical arc plasma may have an electron density of about 10^{12} and a temperature in the neighborhood of an electron volt or so. Hence, the Debye shielding length is less than 10^{-3} cm. It should be noted that the Debye shielding length is a measure of the thickness of the sheath region which develops wherever the plasma is in contact with a solid surface.

A weakly-ionized plasma will be defined as a plasma in which the mean free path for electron-neutral atom collisions and for ion-neutral atom collisions is small compared to the mean free path for appreciable deflections by coulomb collisions between the charged particles. A plasma of this type is particularly susceptible to analysis since the charged-particle conservation conditions will be linear in the particle densities. As a result, the intrinsic diffusion coefficient for electrons in the absence of a magnetic field is

$$D_0^- = \frac{\lambda^- v^-}{3} \qquad (9.14)$$

and that of the ions is

$$D_0^+ = \frac{\lambda^+ v^+}{3}, \qquad (9.15)$$

where λ is the mean free path for collisions with a neutral target and v is the charged-particle velocity. The superscripts $-$ and $+$ denote electrons and ions respectively. In general, the mean free paths will be comparable, while the electron velocity will be very much larger than that of the ion at comparable temperatures. Since the electron-density gradient must be the same as the ion-density gradient, owing to the requirement of space charge neutrality, it is clear that the electrons would tend to stream out of the plasma much more rapidly than the ions.

A situation of this sort is incompatible with the requirement of plasma neutrality and hence electric fields will immediately develop so as to retard the electrons and produce equal streaming losses of electrons and ions from the plasma. The resultant diffusion rate may be calculated by including the added "mobility" of a charged particle due to an applied electric field.

Once again, a one-dimensional argument will be used. Consider a particle which has suffered a collision at the point which is a distance s to the left of a unit area dA located at the origin of Fig. 9.3. Assume that the particle acquires the average thermal velocity v, as a result of this collision, with equal probability to the left and right. It subsequently is accelerated to the right at

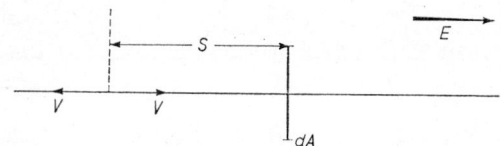

FIG. 9.3. Mobility of a charged particle. .

the constant rate eE/m. It is assumed that the net increment of velocity between collisions is small compared to the thermal velocity. As a result, those particles moving to the left after the collision will not pass through dA, while those moving to the right reach dA with an increased velocity v' given by

$$v' = \sqrt{(v^2 + 2as)}$$

where $a = eE/m$ is the acceleration.
Hence the flux through dA from the left is

$$F_L = \int_0^\infty \frac{n}{2\lambda} \sqrt{(v^2 + 2as)} \exp(-s/\lambda) \, ds.$$

Note that $n/2$ is used rather than $n/6$. The reason for this is the fact that particles moving in all three dimensions are accelerated to the right by the electric field. The desired result may be obtained by expanding the square root term in powers of as/v and subtracting the flux from the right. The first non-vanishing term is

$$F = \frac{na\lambda}{v} \int_0^\infty \frac{s}{\lambda} \exp(-s/\lambda) \, \frac{ds}{\lambda}$$

$$= \frac{na\lambda}{v} = \frac{e\lambda}{mv} \, nE.$$

The mobility μ is defined to be the coefficient of nE in the expression for the flux. (Note that its sign depends on the charge.) Hence

$$F = n\mu E \tag{9.16}$$

and

$$\mu = \frac{e\lambda}{mv}. \tag{9.17}$$

Rewriting this,

$$\mu = \lambda v \cdot \frac{e}{mv^2} = \frac{\lambda v}{3} \frac{e}{kT} = \frac{eD}{kT}, \tag{9.18}$$

where D is the usual diffusion coefficient.

An expression may now be obtained for the common rate of streaming of electrons and ions out of the plasma. The electron flux has the form

$$F^- = - D_0^- \frac{\partial n^-}{\partial x} + n^- \mu_0^- E_x, \tag{9.19}$$

with a similar expression for the ions. Both the density gradient and the electric field are assumed to exist in the x-direction only. The resultant particle conservation equation is

$$\frac{\partial n^-}{\partial t} = - \nabla \cdot F^- = - \frac{\partial F^-}{\partial x}$$

$$\therefore \frac{\partial n^-}{\partial t} = D_0^- \frac{\partial^2 n^-}{\partial x^2} - \mu_0^- \frac{\partial}{\partial x} [n^- E_x], \tag{9.20}$$

while the corresponding expression for the ions is

$$\frac{\partial n^+}{\partial t} = D_0^+ \frac{\partial^2 n^+}{\partial x^2} - \mu_0^+ \frac{\partial}{\partial x} [n^+ E_x]. \tag{9.21}$$

By the basic assumption of near neutrality of the plasma, $n^+ \cong n^- \equiv n$. Thus the electric field term may be eliminated by multiplying Eq. (9.20) by μ_0^+, Eq. (9.21) by μ_0^-, and subtracting. The result is

$$\frac{\partial n}{\partial t} = \frac{\mu_0^+ D_0^- - \mu_0^- D_0^+}{\mu_0^+ - \mu_0^-} \frac{\partial^2 n}{\partial x^2}. \tag{9.22}$$

It is clear that there is an effective diffusion coefficient common to both the electrons and ions. This "ambipolar" quantity is

$$D_0^{\mathrm{AMB}} = \frac{\mu_0{}^+ D_0{}^- - \mu_0{}^- D_0{}^+}{\mu_0{}^+ - \mu_0{}^-} \tag{9.23}$$

Substitution from Eq. (9.18) yields an alternative form

$$D_0^{\mathrm{AMB}} = \frac{D_0{}^+ D_0{}^- [(1/kT_+) + (1/kT_-)]}{(D_0{}^+/kT_+) + (D_0{}^-/kT_-)}.$$

It was pointed out above that for comparable electron and ion temperatures, one has $D_0{}^- \gg D_0{}^+$. Hence Eq. (9.23) reduces in this case to

$$D_0^{\mathrm{AMB}} \simeq 2D_0{}^+. \tag{9.24}$$

Equation (9.24) shows that the effective diffusion coefficient is approximately twice that of the slower component.

The situation when a magnetic field is present is apparently more complicated. However, it is not difficult to carry through a "curved one-dimensional" argument just as in the case of the diffusion coefficient. The result is completely similar. The mobility $\mu_\perp$ across a magnetic field is

$$\mu_\perp = \frac{\mu_0}{1 + (\omega\tau)^2}, \tag{9.25}$$

where μ_0 is the magnetic field-free result given in Eq. (9.17).

In most cases of experimental interest, the plasma density is sufficiently low and the field sufficiently large so that the quantities $(\omega\tau)^2$ for both electrons and ions are very much larger than unity. Since $\omega\tau = \lambda/r_0$ this means that the particles execute very many gyrations in the magnetic field before a collision occurs. [It is clear that if the opposite situation is true, $(\omega\tau)^2 < 1$, the effect of the magnetic field is small and the field-free results of Eqs. (9.14) to (9.24) will apply.]

By Eq. (9.10), the effective diffusion coefficients are:

$$D_\perp{}^+ \simeq \frac{D_0{}^+}{(\omega^+\tau^+)^2}$$

$$D_\perp{}^- = \frac{D_0{}^-}{(\omega^-\tau^-)^2}.$$

Note that these diffusion coefficients vary as the inverse square of the magnetic field strength and depend on the other variables, as follows

$$D \sim \frac{m^2 v^3}{\lambda B^2} = \frac{\sqrt{(m)(kT)^{3/2}}}{\lambda B^2}. \tag{9.26}$$

Hence, for comparable temperatures and mean free paths, the ion diffusion coefficient is very much larger than that of the electrons. Thus

$$D_\perp^+ \gg D_\perp^-. \tag{9.27}$$

The ions tend to diffuse across a magnetic field faster than the electrons, which is the reverse of the behavior in the direction of the field lines. Another way to see this is to recognize that diffusion across the field is by means of the random changes of the location of the center of the Larmor circle of the particle after each collision. This deflection is of the order of the Larmor radius. Hence the heavier particle diffuses faster since it has a larger Larmor radius. The same conclusions hold for the mobility of the particles.

Suppose that the magnetic field lines are infinitely long so that there is no diffusion of electrons or ions in this direction. In this hypothetical case, all diffusion is across the magnetic field, and once again an electric field must develop in this direction so as to equate the electron and ion fluxes and maintain charge neutrality. The argument given in Eqs. (9.19) to (9.23) goes through exactly in this case, except that the subscript 0 is replaced by $\perp$ everywhere. Thus

$$
\begin{aligned}
D_\perp^{\mathrm{AMB}} &= \frac{\mu_\perp^+ D_\perp^- - \mu_\perp^- D_\perp^+}{\mu_\perp^+ - \mu_\perp^-} \\
&= \frac{D_\perp^+ D_\perp^- [(1/kT_+) + (1/kT_-)]}{(D_\perp^+/kT_+) + D_\perp^-/kT_-}.
\end{aligned} \tag{9.28}
$$

By use of Eq. (9.27),

$$D_\perp^{\mathrm{AMB}} \simeq 2D^- \tag{9.29}$$

for equal temperatures. Note that the "ambipolar" rate is again twice that of the slower component.

Diffusion in a finite plasma

The argument just given for "ambipolar" diffusion across a magnetic field can be very misleading when the plasma is of finite extent in the direction of the field lines. In fact, just such an effect accounts for the resolution of a large discrepancy between theory and experiment. This will be described in the next three sections.

Let us now center our attention on a two-dimensional plasma as sketched in Fig. 9.4. The magnetic field lines are in the direction of the x-axis.

FIG. 9.4. Diffusion in a finite plasma.

The plasma is bounded on all sides by a conducting wall of width R and length l. It will be assumed that the mean free path is small compared to the length l, so that particles diffuse along the field lines as well as across the field lines. The electron conservation condition is now

$$\frac{\partial n^-}{\partial t} = D_0^- \frac{\partial^2 n^-}{\partial x^2} - \mu_0^- \frac{\partial}{\partial x}\left(n^- E_x\right) + D_\perp^- \frac{\partial^2 n}{\partial y^2} - \mu_\perp^- \frac{\partial}{\partial y}\left(n^- E_y\right)$$

(9.30)

and that of the ions is

$$\frac{\partial n^+}{\partial t} = D_0^+ \frac{\partial^2 n^+}{\partial x^2} - \mu_0^+ \frac{\partial}{\partial x}\left(n^+ E_x\right) + D_\perp^+ \frac{\partial^2 n}{\partial y^2} - \mu_\perp^+ \frac{\partial}{\partial y}\left(n^+ E_y\right).$$

(9.31)

Now the electric fields in the two directions may be expected to be of the same order of magnitude if R and l are not too different. Since both are spatial derivatives of the same scalar potential V, one might expect

$$E_x = 0 \left[\frac{V}{l} \right]$$

$$E_y = 0 \left[\frac{V}{R} \right]$$

where 0 denotes "of the order of". On the other hand, the coefficients of the mobility terms in Eqs. (9.30) and (9.31) are $\mu_\perp$ and μ_0 and

$$\mu_\perp = \frac{\mu_0}{(\omega\tau)^2} \ll \mu_0.$$

Hence one may neglect the mobility terms in the y-direction in Eqs. (9.30) and (9.31). The remaining term in the electric field, E_x, may be eliminated by assuming near-neutrality of the plasma, $n^+ = n^- = n$, and multiplying Eq. (9.30) by μ_0^+, Eq. (9.31) by μ_0^- and subtracting. The result is

$$\frac{\partial n}{\partial t} = \frac{\mu_0^+ D_0^- - \mu_0^- D_0^+}{\mu_0^+ - \mu_0^-} \frac{\partial^2 n}{\partial x^2} + \frac{\mu_0^+ D_\perp^- - \mu_0^- D_\perp^+}{\mu_0^+ - \mu_0^-} \frac{\partial^2 n}{\partial y^2}.$$

$$(9.32)$$

The effective net diffusion coefficient in the x-direction is

$$D_0 = \frac{\mu_0^+ D_0^- - \mu_0^- D_0^+}{\mu_0^+ - \mu_0} = D_0^{\mathrm{AMB}}$$

which is just the usual ambipolar diffusion coefficient in the field direction (see Eq. 9.23). The effective coefficient across the field is

$$D_\perp = \frac{\mu_0^+ D_\perp^- - \mu_0^- D_\perp^+}{\mu_0^+ - \mu_0^-}. \qquad (9.33)$$

Now $\mu_0^- \gg \mu_0^+$ and $D_\perp^+ \gg D_\perp^-$. Hence

$$D_\perp \cong D_\perp^+. \qquad (9.34)$$

In other words, the effective diffusion coefficient across the field is that of the ions and *not* twice the electron coefficient as would be indicated by a one-dimensional argument such as given in Eq. (9.29) and above. This point will be discussed further below. Equation (9.32) may now be written as:

$$\frac{\partial n}{\partial t} = D_0^{\text{AMB}} \frac{\partial^2 n}{\partial x^2} + D_\perp^+ \frac{\partial^2 n}{\partial y^2}. \tag{9.35}$$

Another situation of experimental interest is the case of the mean free path being large compared to the length l. In this case, electrons and ions stream rather than diffuse to the end walls. The streaming current in the x-direction consists of two parts. One is the direct thermal streaming to the end walls which is equal to $n v_x$ per unit area, where v_x is the average of $|v_x|$ in the plasma. The other component is the increment in velocity caused by acceleration in an electric field. As stated in the previous section, the final velocity v' is related to the initial velocity v by

$$v'^2 = v^2 + 2as,$$

where a is the acceleration and s the distance over which it acts. Assuming this increment to be small compared to the thermal velocity

$$v' \cong v \pm \frac{as}{v}$$

$$\therefore \Delta v = \pm \frac{eE}{m} \frac{l}{2v}$$

since the average distance travelled is $l/2$. Hence the net particle current per unit area streaming out of the plasma is

$$F \cong n v_x + n \frac{el}{2m v_x} E. \tag{9.36}$$

Assume that the net loss of particles arises uniformly from all regions of the plasma. In that case, the conservation equations become

$$\frac{\partial n^-}{\partial t} = D_\perp^- \frac{\partial^2 n^-}{\partial y^2} - \mu_\perp^- \frac{\partial}{\partial y}(n^- E_y) - \frac{n^- v_x^-}{l} + \frac{n^- |e| E_x}{2m^- v_x^-} \tag{9.37}$$

$$\frac{\partial n^+}{\partial t} = D_\perp^+ \frac{\partial^2 n^+}{\partial y^2} - \mu_\perp^+ \frac{\partial}{\partial y}(n^+ E_y) - \frac{n^+ v_x^+}{l} - \frac{n^+ |e| E_x}{2m^+ v_x^+}$$

It is not difficult to show that the mobility term in the y-direction is smaller than the streaming term due to E_x by the approximate factor

$$f = \frac{r_0}{L}\frac{1}{\omega\tau},$$

where r_0 is the Larmor radius and L is a characteristic length in the gas in the y direction. Now L can hardly be smaller than the ion Larmor radius. Hence, once again, one may neglect the mobility term in the y-direction. Eliminating E_x as before, one has:

$$\frac{\partial n}{\partial t} = \frac{m^- v_x^- D_\perp^- + m^+ v_x^+ D_\perp^+}{m^+ v_x^+ + m^- v_x^-}\frac{\partial^2 n}{\partial y^2} - \frac{n}{l}\frac{m^-(v_x^-)^2 + m^+(v_x^+)^2}{m^+ v_x^+ + m^- v_x^-}$$

(9.38)

Now, at equal temperatures, $m^+ v_x^+ \gg m^- v_x^-$. Hence

$$\frac{\partial n}{\partial t} \simeq D_\perp^+ \frac{\partial^2 n}{\partial y^2} - \frac{2n v_x^+}{l}.$$

(9.39)

Once again the effective diffusion coefficient across the plasma is that of the ions, while the effective streaming velocity out of the plasma is twice that of the slower ions.

The short circuit

The significance of the previous results is that diffusion across a magnetic field is not ambipolar in the presence of end walls[42]. The essential reason is that space is no longer isotropic in the presence of a magnetic field. It is no longer necessary that the individual currents balance out to zero in each direction in order to maintain space-charge neutrality. Instead all that is necessary is that the total current in all directions balance to zero.

Thus, if ions move out more rapidly in the y-direction, as is their tendency, the small electric fields which develop affect the currents moving in the direction of the magnetic field lines long

---

[42] A. SIMON, Ambipolar Diffusion in a Magnetic Field, *Phys. Rev.* **98**, 317 (1955).

before they have an appreciable effect on the currents in the
y-direction. This is because the mobility is so much larger in the
x-direction. Thus, small readjustments in the currents flowing to
the end walls maintain neutrality, and allow the ions to move
across the field at their intrinsic rate. It is as if there were an
electron short-circuit along the field lines and through the end
walls to counteract any tendency to build up space charge.

Experimental results

A series of experiments have been performed at Oak Ridge to
test these considerations[43]. A plasma was formed by use of an
arc discharge in a cylindrical chamber. The experimental setup

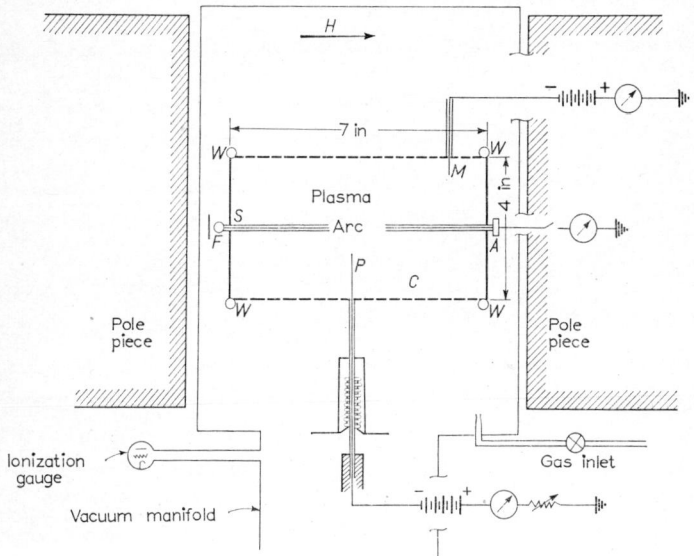

FIG. 9.5. Schematic diagram of the diffusion apparatus in the
j magnet.

is shown in Fig. 9.5. The magnetic field is along the axis of the
cylinder. The plasma ion densities are measured inside the

[43] A. SIMON and R. V. NEIDIGH, Diffusion of Ions in a Plasma Across
a Magnetic Field, ORNL–1890 (Nov., 1955).

cylinder by means of a carbon probe. The electron source is a heated filament biased about 100 volts negative. Electrons are accelerated along magnetic field lines into the field-free region within the cylinder. Ions are formed along the axis of the cylinder and diffuse out into the plasma region.

The experiment was performed using nitrogen gas at pressures of about 10^{-3} mm Hg. The arc current measured at the anode varied from 0.2 to 1.0 ampere depending on the combination of pressure and arc voltage used. The probe was biased 20 volts negative and this is on the flat portion of its characteristic curve. It was assumed that ion density is proportional to probe current.

The measured ion density decreased exponentially outward from the arc column. This is to be expected. Consider Eq. (9.35) for steady-state conditions. Then

$$\frac{\partial^2 n}{\partial y^2} = -\frac{D_0^{\text{AMB}}}{D_\perp^+} \frac{\partial^2 n}{\partial x^2}.$$

Assume separability of the flux,

$$n(x, y) = n(y)N(x),$$

and require the ion density to vanish at the end walls. Then

$$N(x) = N_0 \sin\left(\frac{\pi x}{l}\right)$$

and

$$\frac{\partial^2 n}{\partial y^2} = \frac{\pi^2 D_0^{\text{AMB}}}{l^2 D_\perp^+} n. \tag{9.40}$$

Hence

$$n = A \exp(-y/y_0) + B \exp(+y/y_0)$$

with

$$y_0 = \frac{l}{\pi}\sqrt{\frac{D_\perp^+}{D_0^{\text{AMB}}}}. \tag{9.41}$$

Finally, since the sources are entirely at the axis, the coefficient B must vanish. In cylindrical coordinates, this result becomes

$$n = AK_0\left(\frac{r}{r_0}\right)$$

where K_0 is the usual Bessel function. When $r \gg r_0$,

$$n \sim \frac{1}{\sqrt{r}} \exp(-r/r_0) \qquad (9.42)$$

and

$$r_0 = \frac{l}{\pi} \sqrt{\frac{D_\perp^+}{D_0^{AMB}}}. \qquad (9.43)$$

The basic experiment consists in measuring the characteristic e-folding length, r_0, as a function of magnetic field strength and gas pressure. Note by Eqs. (9.10) and (9.23) that r_0 is inversely proportional to the field strength. This result is true even in the case of free streaming to the end walls. In the steady state, Eq. (9.39) becomes

$$\frac{\partial^2 n}{\partial y^2} = n \frac{2v_x^+}{lD_\perp^+} \qquad (9.44)$$

The corresponding solution in cylindrical geometry is

$$n = AK_0\left(\frac{r}{r_0}\right) \simeq \frac{1}{\sqrt{r}} \exp(-r/r_0) \qquad (9.45)$$

with

$$r_0 = \sqrt{\frac{lD_\perp^+}{2v_x^+}}. \qquad (9.46)$$

Again $r_0 \sim 1/B$.

The first series of experiments were intended to verify that $D_\perp \sim 1/B^2$ and hence $r_0 \sim 1/B$. A typical set of measurements is shown in Fig. 9.6. Note that at each field strength, the ion density is an exponential function of the radial distance. The reciprocal of the e-folding length $(1/r_0)$ is plotted as a function of B in Fig. 9.7. The data clearly favor the linear variation of slope with magnetic field strength, and hence, $D_\perp$ varies as $1/B^2$. It seems clear that a $1/B$ dependence of $D_\perp$, which would imply a $\sqrt{B}$ dependence of $1/r_0$ is excluded.

A second series of measurements[44] investigated the pressure dependence of r_0 for fixed magnetic field. In the case of diffusion

---

[44] R. V. NEIDIGH, Some Experiments Relating Ion Diffusion in a Plasma to the Neutral Gas Density in the Presence of a Magnetic Field, ORNL–2024 (May, 1956).

to the end walls, Eqs. (9.10), (9.24), and (9.43) show that $r_0 \sim 1/\lambda \sim P$. Where there is free streaming to the end walls, Eqs. (9.10), (9.11), and (9.46) show that $r_0 \sim \sqrt{(1/\lambda)} \sim \sqrt{P}$. Both of these variations have been observed by using a shortened arc chamber ($\lambda > l$) and a lengthened arc chamber ($\lambda < l$).

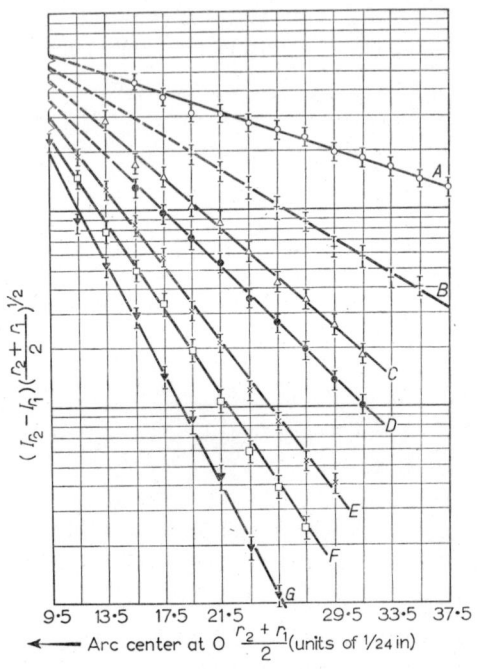

FIG. 9.6. Ion current to the differential probe ($I_{r_2} - I_{r_1}$), multiplied by the square root of the radial probe position, $[(r_2 + r_1)/2]^{1/2}$ as a function of probe position, $(r_2 + r_1)/2$.

A third measurement considered the effect of placing magnetic mirrors at the ends of the arc chamber. It can be shown[45] that r_0 becomes independent of pressure in this case, and this, too, was verified experimentally.

[45] A. SIMON, The Influence of End Mirrors, High Density, and Long Tube Length on Radial Diffusion, ORNL–1960 (Sept., 1955).

The final item is the question of the magnitude of the diffusion coefficient. This may be determined from the observed values of the e-folding length. The neutral density at a pressure of

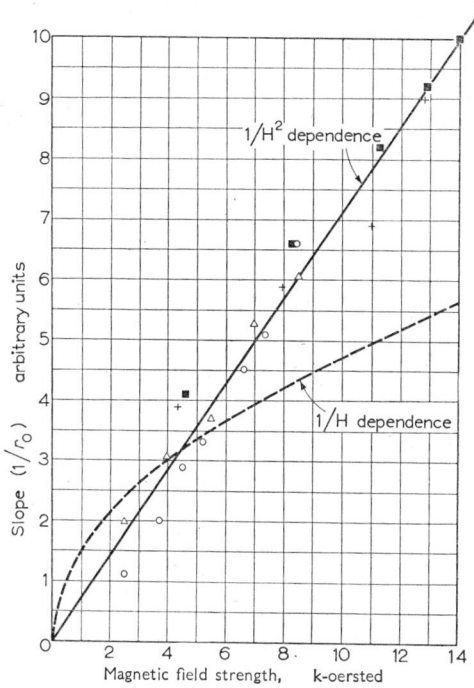

FIG. 9.7. Plot of slopes $1/r_0$ as a function of magnetic field strength. The data clearly indicate a $1/H^2$ dependence. The broken line would represent a $1/H$ dependence, fitted at 4000 oersteds.

1.5 mm Hg and room temperature is about 5×10^{13} cm^{-3}. The electron-neutral atom and ion-neutral atom cross-sections are very poorly known. A rough estimate, judging from some of the assembled cross-section data[46], is as follows:

$$\sigma^- \cong 3 \times 10^{-15} \text{ cm}^2$$
$$\sigma^+ \cong 7 \times 10^{-15} \text{ cm}^2.$$

---

[46] S. C. BROWN and W. P. ALLIS, Basic Data of Electrical Discharges, Tech. Report 283, Research Lab. of Electronics, MIT (June, 1954).

M

These estimates assume an ion and electron temperature in the plasma of about 2 volts. The temperature estimate is itself quite uncertain and is based on the variation of the probe characteristic with applied voltage. (It should be noted that particles with larger collision cross sections are more likely to be found out in the plasma since they diffuse more rapidly away from the arc.) The mean free paths corresponding to these numbers are

$$\lambda^+ \cong 3 \text{ cm.}$$
$$\lambda^- \cong 6.5 \text{ cm.} \tag{9.47}$$

The coulomb mean free path is about 14 cm for an ionization of 1%. The percentage ionization is unknown but is believed to be considerably less than 10%. It is clear that the effects of electron–ion collisions are not entirely negligible. Nevertheless, these effects will be ignored. It may be that some of the remaining numerical discrepancies are due to this factor.

A typical value of r_0 is 0.7 cm at $B = 4000$ gauss. Inserting this value in Eq. (9.43) (diffusion to end walls) yields:

$$D_\perp = 1.54 \times 10^{-2} D_0^{\text{AMB}}$$

Now
$$D_0^{\text{AMB}} = 2D_0{}^+ = \tfrac{2}{3} \lambda^+ v^+.$$

At a temperature of about 2 volts,

$$v^+ \cong 3 \times 10^5 \text{ cm/sec.} \tag{9.48}$$

Hence
$$D_\perp = 9.2 \times 10^3 \text{ cm}^2/\text{sec.} \tag{9.49}$$

This is the experimental value of the effective diffusion coefficient across a magnetic field. This is to be compared with $D_\perp{}^+$, which the short-circuit theory predicts. Now, at 4000 gauss

$$\omega^+ = \frac{eH}{m^+c} = 1.3 \times 10^6 \text{ sec}^{-1}$$

$$\tau^+ = \frac{\lambda^+}{v^+} = 10^{-5} \text{ sec}$$

and
$$(\omega\tau)^+ = 13.$$

Hence,

$$D_\perp{}^+ = \frac{\lambda^+ v^+}{3[(\omega\tau)^+]^2} = 1.75 \times 10^3 \text{ cm}^2/\text{sec.} \tag{9.50}$$

This is in fair agreement with the experimental result in Eq. (9.49). The factor of 5 may be due to uncertainties in the cross sections, ion temperature, and the effects of coulomb collisions. The importance of this result is the fact that there is an order of magnitude agreement with experiment. This point is discussed in the next section.

Diffusion by "plasma oscillations"

Early experiments at Berkeley[47] by Bohm, Burhop, Massey, and Williams had seemed to indicate an anomalously large ion diffusion rate across a magnetic field. The experimental method was completely similar to that described above. An e-folding length of about 0.3 cm was measured at a fixed field value of 3700 gauss. This yielded an effective diffusion coefficient across a magnetic field of about 3×10^3 cm²/sec, which is in good agreement with the experimental results at Oak Ridge. Unfortunately, the theoretical analysis omitted the "short-circuit" effect by not including the effects of electric fields in the direction of the magnetic field lines. As a result, the predicted coefficient was believed to be only 20 cm²/sec, in sharp disagreement with the experimental result.

In order to resolve this apparent discrepancy, Bohm[47] postulated that the observed diffusion was caused by the action of a new mechanism. He stated that plasma oscillations were producing diffusion and that the corresponding diffusion coefficient is

$$D_{\perp}^{\text{BOHM}} \simeq \frac{D_0}{16\omega\tau} = \frac{10^8 kT}{16B} \text{ cm}^2/\text{sec}, \qquad (9.51)$$

where kT is in electron-volts and B in gauss. No theoretical derivation of this result is available.

The magnitude of the coefficient at $kT = 2$ volts and $B = 4000$ gauss is about 3×10^3 in agreement with the experimental value. Unfortunately, owing to the press of wartime

---

[47] *The Characteristics of Electrical Discharges in Magnetic Fields* (ed. by A. GUTHRIE and R. K. WAKERLING), p. 201, McGraw-Hill, New York (1949).

conditions, no attempt was made to verify the $1/B$ dependence predicted in Eq. (9.51). The experiments at Oak Ridge seem to rule out any such dependence and what's more, the inclusion of the short-circuit effect resolves any large numerical discrepancy. It goes without saying that a $1/B$ dependence of the diffusion rate would be disastrous to the economics of the proposed Sherwood devices. Incidentally, this result should not be construed as indicating the absence of plasma oscillations. However, it does imply that they may have little or no effect on diffusion.

Further experiments in this field are under way at Oak Ridge and Los Alamos. The proposed experiment at Los Alamos will involve a very long tube so as to attempt to eliminate the short-circuit effect. The decay of the plasma of an afterglow will be observed. At Oak Ridge, recent observations of the cylindrical arc at low pressure have produced an unusual oscillatory state[48]. A complete understanding of this so-called "Mode II" state has not yet been achieved.

Summary

The observed diffusion rates of ions in a weakly-ionized plasma across a magnetic field may be understood on the basis of classical collision-diffusion theory. However, the diffusion rate is not ambipolar owing to the short-circuit effect of currents flowing in the direction of the field lines to the end walls. It is not necessary to invoke any additional diffusion mechanisms, such as plasma oscillations.

FULLY-IONIZED PLASMA

The treatment of a fully-ionized plasma is in some ways easier than that of a weakly-ionized plasma since there are only two kinds of particles, electrons and ions, whose interaction law (coulomb scattering) is well known. On the other hand, the basic conservation equations are non-linear which is always a

---

[48] R. V. NEIDIGH and A. SIMON, Extension of Ion Diffusion Experiments, *Conference on Controlled Thermonuclear Reactions*, TID–7520 (Sept., 1956).

difficulty. A great deal of information may be obtained by use of the two-fluid or hydromagnetic equations of motion of the system. This is the method used by Spitzer[35] to obtain so many useful results. The diffusion rate will be obtained below by this scheme. Kinetic considerations will be appealed to only to explain some apparent paradoxes which arise.

First-order diffusion

The force equation for a plasma has already been given in Eq. (8.4). In steady state, neglecting electric fields, gravity and a non-linear term in the mass velocity, this equation becomes

$$\nabla P = \mathbf{j} \times \mathbf{B}. \tag{9.52}$$

Similarly, Ohm's law, Eq. (8.6) becomes

$$\mathbf{j} = \frac{\sigma}{c^2} \mathbf{v} \times \mathbf{B}, \tag{9.53}$$

where the plasma is assumed to have zero charge density and where σ is the conductivity. Substituting Eq. (9.53) in Eq. (9.52) yields

$$\nabla P = \frac{\sigma}{c^2} [(\mathbf{v} \cdot \mathbf{B})\mathbf{B} - B^2 \mathbf{v}]. \tag{9.54}$$

This shows that there is a component of the mass velocity at right angles to the direction of the magnetic field and that this velocity is proportional to the pressure gradient. Thus

$$\mathbf{v}_\perp = -\frac{c^2}{\sigma B^2} \nabla_\perp P. \tag{9.55}$$

Note that the diffusion rate is inversely proportional to the square of the magnetic field. At constant temperature

$$n\mathbf{v}_\perp = -\frac{nkTc^2}{\sigma B^2} \nabla n,$$

where n is the particle density. Hence, the effective diffusion coefficient is

$$D_\perp = \frac{nkTc^2}{\sigma B^2} \tag{9.56}$$

The conductivity has already been estimated from simple kinetic considerations in Chapter VII (see discussion immediately after Eq. (7.36.) It was shown that

$$\sigma \simeq \frac{ne^2\lambda}{mv}, \tag{9.57}$$

where λ is the mean free path for electron–ion collisions. Substituting in Eq. (9.56), we have

$$D_\perp \simeq \frac{mvc^2kT}{e^2\lambda B^2}$$

$$= \frac{m^2v^3c^2}{3e^2\lambda B^2}.$$

Now

$$\omega^2 = \frac{e^2B^2}{m^2c^2}$$

and

$$\tau = \lambda/v.$$

Hence

$$D_\perp \simeq \frac{\lambda v}{3}\frac{1}{(\omega\tau)^2} \tag{9.58}$$

which is entirely similar to the previous result for a weakly-ionized plasma.

The similarity ceases at this point, however. The particle flux must be the same for *both* electrons and ions. To see this, note that by Eq. (9.52) there can be no component of the current in the direction of the density gradient. Thus

$$\mathbf{j}\cdot\nabla P = 0$$

and the electrons and ions diffuse at the same rate. It can easily be shown that the next current divergence also vanishes.

The explanation of this effect can be found in a simple kinetic picture. The center of gyration of a charged particle in a magnetic field is at point r_c which is determined by the instantaneous position and velocity of the particle. Thus

$$\mathbf{r}_c - \mathbf{r} = \frac{mc}{eB^2}\mathbf{v}\times\mathbf{B}, \tag{9.59}$$

where $\mathbf{r}$ is the particle position and $\mathbf{v}$ its velocity. Now, when two particles collide elastically, the net momentum change must be zero.

$$\Delta(m_1v_1) = -\Delta(m_2v_2).$$

Hence, it is clear from Eq. (9.59) that the centers of gyration will shift equally in the same direction for a collision between an electron and an ion ($e_1 = -e_2$) and equally in opposite directions for an ion–ion or electron–electron ($e_1 = e_2$) collision. Since the resistivity and hence the diffusion is due to electron–ion collisions it is clear that the electron and ion diffusion rates must be equal, at least to first order in an expansion in powers of the Larmor radius. A similar conclusion holds for the diffusion rates produced by an electric field.

Like-particle diffusion

The results derived above are correct to first order in an expansion in powers of r_0/L where r_0 is the Larmor radius and L a characteristic length in the gas. Since these first-order results arose directly from the fluid equations, Eqs. (9.52) and (9.53), it is clear that this first-order approximation has been built-in to start with. The obvious approximation which has been made is the replacement of the stress tensor by an isotropic pressure. It can be shown that the off-diagonal elements of the stress tensor are smaller than the diagonal elements by the factor r_0/L.

There is an obvious way to demonstrate that the scalar pressure neglects higher-order effects. Consider the case of diffusion in a gas of like charged particles. In this one-fluid situation, there is no Ohm's law but there is still a force equation.

$$\nabla P = \mathbf{j} \times \mathbf{B}. \tag{9.60}$$

However, the current and the mass velocity are uniquely related. Thus

$$\mathbf{j} = \frac{ne}{c}\mathbf{v}. \tag{9.61}$$

Substituting this in the force equation yields

$$\nabla P = \frac{ne}{c} \mathbf{v} \times \mathbf{B}. \qquad (9.62)$$

Thus Eqs. (9.62) and (9.60) indicate that there can be no mass velocity or current in the direction of a density gradient in a simple gas (i.e. a gas of like particles).

On physical grounds, this result cannot be correct to all orders. The apparent paradox has been resolved by including the off-diagonal elements in the stress tensor[49]. The resulting diffusion rate was found to be dependent on the third derivative of the particle density and on the inverse fourth power of the magnetic field. This is to be expected for a result which should be of higher order than ordinary diffusion by the factor $(r_0/L)^2$. The result is

$$v_\perp = \frac{3}{32} \frac{r_0^4}{\tau} \frac{\mathrm{d}}{\mathrm{d}x} \left[\frac{1}{n} \frac{\mathrm{d}^2 n}{\mathrm{d}x^2} \right] \qquad (9.63)$$

where r_0 is the Larmor radius. This rate is usually smaller than that due to electron–ion collisions but could conceivably be as large under some conditions. Longmire and Rosenbluth[50] have recently derived this result by starting from the Fokker–Planck equation and have shown that the rate vanishes identically in first order. Their final result differs from that of Eq. (9.63) by the numerical factor 4/3. It may be that this discrepancy is inherent in the different approximations which are used.

A similar higher order result [$\sim (\mathrm{d}^2 E)/(\mathrm{d}x^2)$] holds for diffusion of like particles produced by an electric field.

[49] A. SIMON, Diffusion of Like Particles Across a Magnetic Field, *Phys. Rev.* **100**, 1557 (1955).

[50] C. L. LONGMIRE and M. N. ROSENBLUTH, Diffusion of Charged Particles Across a Magnetic Field, *Phys. Rev.* **103**, 507 (1956).

NAME INDEX

SUBJECT INDEX

179